The Instrument Pilot's Library
• Volume Three •

Charts
and
Plates

by
The Editors of *IFR* and *IFR Refresher*

Belvoir Publications, Inc.
Greenwich, Connecticut

ISBN: 1-879620-19-7

Printed and bound in the United States of America by Arcata Graphics, Fairfield, Pennsylvania.

Contents

Preface

The third volume of the *Instrument Pilot's Library* takes a close look at the tools of the IFR pilot's trade, the charts and plates used to navigate safely through today's complex airspace structure.

We begin with an analysis of the three charting systems instrument pilots have to choose from: Jeppesen, NOS, and Air Chart Systems. Each has its strengths and weaknesses, which we cover in detail, Also, we'll discuss the recent and upcoming changes made to the NOS products that make them more desirable, along with the price increases that take away some of their competitive edge. We'll also hear from the users of the various systems and find out what their preferences are. Lastly, we have a rare interview with E.B. Jeppesen, the man who is personally responsible for approach and en route charts as we know them today.

The second section of the book takes a look at what's behind the creation of approach plates: how approaches are created and the standards to which they're held, and a description of how they're inspected and maintained. There's also coverage of the (hopefully) upcoming flood of GPS approaches that may someday supplant the existing VOR-ILS system.

The last section takes a close look at a wide variety of chart details, from an examination of flight planning aids to a discussion of the traps that lurk in many approach plates, and how best to avoid them.

Charts and Plates is not a textbook on how to read a chart. That information can be found in any instrument flying manual. Rather, our aim is to provide you with the knowledge you won't find anywhere else—not to give you the basics, but how to make the best possible use of the basics once you've mastered them.

• Section One •

Chart Systems

Which System is Best?

R ight up front we have to tell you that there is no simple answer to the question, "Which charts should I use?" Each of the three systems available has its own strengths and weaknesses, and when it comes right down to it the choice is as much a matter of personal preference as anything else. We've got our own opinions (which we'll share here), but the reader should be aware that what's right for us may not be right for you.

That said, this first chapter is devoted to a comparison of the three basic chart systems available to U.S. pilots: Jeppesen, government (NOS) and Howie Keefe's Air Chart Systems. Since the latter product is actually a reprinted, repackaged version of the government charts and plates, and since it is radically different from the other two services, we'll look at it separately.

Later chapters will cover other services like trip kits and RNAV services, but for now we'll examine only the basic product: charts and plates.

First up is a close look at the two systems you're most likely to encounter, Jeppesen and NOS.

Jeppesen or NOS?

Whether you're a wet-ticket whuffo or a gnarly old pro with a few kilo hours in hard IMC, you've got to have a set of decent, up-to-date charts and plates. For nearly as long as pilots have been mucking around in the clouds, there have really been only two choices: Jeppesen-Sanderson's well-known Airway Manuals and the government charts put out by the National Ocean Service.

A third service—Air Chart Systems—repackages the government stuff with some unique products of its own. We'll take a look at that system later on but for now, the question is: Jeppesen or NOS?

The principal difference between the two is that Jeppesen packages its service in a seven-ring binder system which (in the basic service) the user must update on his own, every two weeks. NOS plates have been issued in bound booklets every 56 days. (As of May, 1994, NOS is switching to looseleaf plates; more on this later.) When the new ones arrive, the pilot simply trashes the old set.

A couple of years ago Jeppesen responded to those who liked the product but hated the updating process with a relatively new variant called the Q-service in which a whole new set of charts and plates is sent out on the regular 56-day cycle. The user then chucks the old set and puts the new one in the binder, just like NOS. This is a very expensive service, however; far more costly than any of the alternatives. For the purposes of this discussion, we'll compare the garden-variety manual-update Jeppesen service to NOS, since these are the two that compete on price. For the pilot who concludes that Jeppesen is the way to go and is willing to cough up the extra cash, the Q-service is always available.

A detailed comparison of the two systems reveals some subtle differences and perhaps some surprises, especially with regard to price and accuracy.

First, the bottom line

Many pilots we know—neophytes and veterans alike—base their chart buying decisions solely on price and, to a lesser extent, on convenience of revisions. Unless you've done a feature-by-feature comparison of both systems, this makes a certain sense. After all, NOS produces serviceable IFR charts that appear to be cheaper than Jeppesen and there's little question that the government charts are easier to keep current. However, as we'll point out, the discerning IFR pilot who really wants and needs accurate data may actually pay more for NOS charts.

Just how much you pay depends on where you're based, how far afield your IFR trips take you and whether you buy charts piecemeal or by subscription. To keep things simple, we'll compare only the costs of subscriptions. Jeppesen is available only by subscription anyway (except for trip kits) and we think buying NOS products piecemeal almost guarantees you'll miss important revision data.

As of January, 1994, NOS prices increased quite a bit, so that now basic coverage from the two services costs roughly the same. It varies by region, though, due mainly to the way the two services divvy up the states. For example, 1994 subscription prices for Jepp Northeast coverage is $135. NOS coverage (five en routes and three terminal books) costs about $160. For the Southeast, which NOS covers with only three en routes, the situation is reversed: Jepp $133; NOS $115. For complete U.S. coverage, the price gap is larger; Jeppesen charges $385 a year to NOS's $458.

There are startup costs for Jeppesen that NOS does not have; an initial contents to get you started (varies by region: full U.S. is $141, Northeast and Southeast are $46 each, Northwest and Southwest, $27 each), plus special binders to hold the charts the cost of the binders which are $21.70 each for vinyl, $48.30 for the top-of-the-line leather. Typically, regional service requires two to three binders, coverage for the entire U.S. a weighty seven binders. If your taste runs to leather, the binders alone for U.S. coverage will cost nearly $350. Check the discounters, however, for lower prices on binders, or consider the mid-line "Duraflo" synthetic binders, which cost just over $30 and are far more durable than the vinyl ones.

Hidden costs

Let's take a typical example, such as a pilot starting out with northeast coverage. A Jeppesen customer will pay $183 for the initial coverage and a year of revisions plus $21.70 each for the two binders. That's a total of $226.40 for the first year, followed by $135 each year for revisions. The equivalent coverage for NOS comes to $160 or so for the first year and for every year thereafter, assuming no price increases. Initially, then, NOS looks to be cheaper; it'll take about 2-1/2 years for the services to reach parity.

But there's a catch. Ordering just the NOS coverage includes enroute charts and plates, but it doesn't include printed notams, which is how NOS communicates a great deal of its revisions. In a rather low-key paragraph in its catalog, NOS lists printed notams (and the Airport/Facility Directory) as a supplemental publication "essential to the safety of flight."

Important amendments to plates and charts are carried in printed notams and both NOS and the FAA assume that pilots subscribe. Of course, hardly anybody does. Pilots who buy plates piecemeal from the local pilot shop often aren't even aware of printed notams.

If you add the cost of notams (January '94 price $208 per year) to an NOS subscription—and we would argue that you should—that same northeast subscription will cost considerably more than the equivalent Jeppesen service.

What the basic service includes

As we've pointed out, a subscription to NOS is basically just charts and plates, no extras. RNAV approaches do come standard in NOS booklets, a service for which Jeppesen subscribers have to pay extra. Jeppesen customers, on the other hand, do get some important features NOS users don't, some of which are related to the binder revision system.

Two features we like are Jeppesen's notam service and its listing of IFR preferred routes. Because Jeppesen sends revisions every two weeks, important changes that NOS relegates to printed notams are automatically incorporated on Jeppesen's plates. Changes too trivial to require a new plate (or revisions to enroute charts) are communicated to Jeppesen subscribers via its own version of the printed notams. These are sent along with the fortnightly revisions and are essentially an edited version of the government notam lists. Because they aren't complete, Jeppesen does recommend that pilots subscribe to the federal notams. But frankly, we think this is overkill, as Jeppesen's editing seems to delete only the really obscure stuff. In any case, if you decide not to subscribe to the notam book at all, we think you'll have more complete and timely information with a Jeppesen subscription.

Other extras included in Jeppesen service include tabs for the binder, chart wallets, a plotter, a more complete legend with quite a bit of IFR flight data, a flight planning chart, separate terminal and area charts, and free replacement for lost or damaged charts.

NOS users get area charts as well, but only subscribers get them. If you buy piecemeal, you'll pay extra, if your supplier even carries the area charts. In our experience, many do not. Other accessories—the NOS Flight Case Planning chart and terminal charts—are available at extra cost. And if your NOS enroute chart gets blasted off the wing by a passing jet, you'll have to buy a new one, no free replacements.

Comparing the enroutes

Both services cover the U.S. via a series of charts, one set for the low-altitude airways below 18,000 feet, another for the J-routes. We'll limit our discussion to low-altitudes, but first, a mention of the planning charts. Both Jeppesen and NOS produce planning charts.

Jeppesen subscribers get theirs free—either the U.S. FP/LO or the FP/HI. The chart includes principal airways, mileage tables, charts with three-letter identifiers for weather briefing plus odds and ends such as a flight plan form and aircraft equipment codes. In short, the FP is just the thing for briefing via DUAT or airfiling on the run. Too bad it's such an underused chart.

The NOS equivalent is the Flight Case Planning chart. It's organized similarly but doesn't have nearly the weather briefing and flight planning info that Jeppesen's FP does. Worse, you pay extra for it.

As for the enroute charts themselves, the first thing most users notice is that the NOS charts are bigger than Jeppesen's (ten panels versus nine) and that they're printed on heavier paper.

Which paper is better is a matter of opinion: some find that the government charts hold up better under heavy use, while others like the ease of handling the Jepp versions offer. In particular, the NOS charts tend to wear and rip at the spots where the horizontal and vertical folds intersect (there's a corollary of Murphy's Law which states that this spot will always be in the center of a critical feature on the chart). The thinner Jepp chart paper, being easier to fold, doesn't have this problem.

However, the paper used for the Jepp charts is, overall, flimsier. It's all too easy to accidentally tear it or poke a hole in it with a sharp pencil.

By the way, Air Chart Systems doesn't have the problem of wear caused by folding and refolding since their enroutes are bound in a book format.

Aggravating the durability issue is the fact that Jeppesen charts aren't replaced on the 56-day airspace cycle, as are NOS products. Instead, Jeppesen users get new enroutes only when sufficient changes have occurred to justify a new chart. That can sometimes take two or three airspace cycles so not only do they wear out faster, Jeppesen charts have to last longer. Of course, you can always order a free replacement, if you don't mind waiting a few days for it to arrive.

The smaller size of the Jepp charts simplifies handling somewhat. Unfolding a NOS enroute (which, by the way, is the same size as a sectional) simply takes up more precious cockpit space. Of course, it is normally refolded to a more manageable size, but there's always the awkwardness of filling the cockpit with a paper monster before it's brought under control.

In the cockpit, the pros and cons of each system are pretty close to an even wash. In our view, it's more a matter of personal taste than one system being vastly superior to the other. But there are some fine points worth niggling over, nonetheless.

One thing we like about the NOS charts is that the legend is printed right on the chart cover. This is quite handy if you're droning along in the muck amusing yourself with some chart review. It's rather harder to do with the Jeppesen charts, since the legend is filed in one of those fat binders, which is probably on the backseat or the floor.

Of course, if you do bother to dig out the Jepp legend, it has lots more to read. Besides explaining the symbols, there's a chart glossary that delves into the minutiae of IFR flying, plus lots of advice on operational considerations.

While the legend is nice to have, the Jepp wins for its clever indexing system. Both NOS and Jepp charts have indices that are supposed to help you pick out the most inconspicuous airports from the background clutter. In this regard, Jeppesen's famous Zigdex is the hands down winner.

The Zigdex is Jeppesen's method for locating chart panels easily. The upper edge of a Jepp enroute is trimmed at a slight angle so that, when folded, a small area at the top of each panel is visible as though in a display case.

On the panels of the chart that appear on the outside when it's folded, airports are listed alphabetically. Each is given a panel location, such as p6C. The panel numbers are depicted in the Zigdex on the back of the folded chart. The angled trim line makes it easy to open to a specific panel by slipping one's finger into the chart at the appropriate place in the Zigdex.

Once opened, the chart is a reasonably easy to handle 14 inches high by 10 wide, divided into four subpanels. An NOS chart opened to one of the panels is 20 inches high by 10 wide, without the subdivision.

Opening panel six on a Jepp chart, for example, the airport would be found in subpanel C, the lower left corner. On NOS charts, airports are located only by main panel, so your search has to cover an area nearly six times as large.

The new, improved NOS enroutes

In late 1993, NOS overhauled its enroute chart format, and, we feel, improved it considerably.

The most noticeable change is one that we heartily applaud: the addition of a third and fourth color. Previously both NOS and Jepp charts were printed in only two colors; blue and green for Jepps, blue and brown for NOS. While this is better than one color (particularly in crowded areas), the additional colors make the chart far easier to interpret, in our opinion.

The NOS charts are now printed in black, brown, blue and green. Where certain information had once been printed only in blue, it's now either black or blue. Being able to visually separate, say, airport frequency information (blue) from the ILS and VOR frequency boxes (black) improves readability over the old chart, where everything was printed in blue.

The color is also used to good effect near shorelines. The previous shoreline symbol was a shaded blue area which made the blue type printed over it hard to read. Water is now green, which contrasts nicely with the blue or black textual information.

NOS has also decluttered the enroute chart, removing or resizing some symbols, and altering the typeface and presentation of text to make it easier to read. Overall, the change is for the better.

Chart clutter

With its obsession for aeronautical detail, Jeppesen charts have the reputation for being a little too cluttered. Some of this detail—lat-lon for principal intersections, for example, is occasionally useful but sometimes it just gets in the way. As with the new NOS charts, in recent years Jeppesen has gotten rid of much of the needless detail from both charts and plates.

To some degree, both Jeppesen and NOS have accomplished this decluttering by manipulating the chart scales. Both services publish area charts—large scale plots of major metro areas. NOS has 13 area charts, printed on a single chart called the A-1/A-2. Coverage includes most cities with Class B areas but, inexplicably, not New York. By contrast, with 32 area charts, all but one a separate mini-chart punched for the binders, Jeppesen has nearly three times the coverage. The only area chart not punched is the 1/2, which covers the northeast corridor from Boston to Washington.

Even with the new NOS format, chart for chart we don't see much difference in either readability or information. Again, it comes down to a matter of opinion.

Another NOS feature we've always liked is that airport runway length and ATIS frequencies are given on the chart rather than just the airport elevation, as on Jeppesen charts. This is convenient if you want to keep apprised of current weather along your route in case you have to get on the ground in a hurry. Jepps has the data, along with tower and other frequencies, on the communications tab, where it's harder to find.

If you use your IFR charts for visual navigation—not always the best idea—NOS products are a bit better at depicting airspace features like Class B and C areas, which are represented by barely discernable pale blue dots on Jeppesen charts. On the other hand, NOS doesn't show many obstructions, while Jeppesen plots many (but not all) obstructions with little green tower symbols with the MSL elevation alongside.

Comparing the plates

While we feel comfortable using either NOS or Jeppesen enroutes, we see some important differences between the two systems when it comes to plates.

First, in basic organization, Jeppesen products seem more logical and intuitive. As we mentioned, the government plates come in regional or state volumes arranged alphabetically by city name, thus,

Atlantic City, N.J. follows Ashland, Va. in the NE-3 booklet. Because the city name is printed at the top of the page, you can't really rifle through the booklet to find the plate you want; you have to refer to the index, which is illogically located not right at the front of the book but after the inoperative components and landing minima tables. In the Jepps binder, you simply locate the state tab and turn to the proper plate, without need for an index. Further, the NOS index has you hopping around the booklet to look up take-off minimums, alternate minimums and radar approach minimums, each of which is in its own section.

Until recently, NOS SIDs and STARs were in a separate booklet but now they're incorporated in the same booklet as the approaches. Unfortunately, the STARs are at the front of the booklet arranged alphabetically by procedure name while the SIDs are in the body of the booklet, with the approaches. Why not put SIDs and STARs together, as Jeppesen does? This would greatly simplify planning, as would having the take-off, alternate minima and inoperative components tables all in the same place, preferably with the appropriate approach.

In a survey we ran in *IFR*, many readers complained about the poor quality paper NOS uses; it's newsprint. But just as many noted that Jeppesen plates, printed on a flimsy but whiter paper than NOS uses, tend to rip at the weak areas near the binding holes. We would say pay your money and take your choice. NOS sends new plates every 56 days; Jeppesen will replace damaged plates for free, within reason. Or, you can pay a little extra and buy plastic chart protector sleeves for the Jeppesen plates. Most pilots keep their most-used plates in the sleeves all the time, and put protectors on other plates as needed.

Along with the revised enroutes, NOS has changed the approach plates for 1994. As we mentioned, instead of the traditional bound booklet, as of May 1994 they'll only be available as a looseleaf book. Users will have to buy the rings, at $2 a set, to hold the book together. If the new book is like the test books produced a few years back, it'll be bound along the top edge of the plates, just as the old books were.

This new format has two advantages over the old: first, the book will now lie flat, and second, it's easy to remove individual plates and put them in chart wallets so the whole book doesn't need to be used.

Clarity and clutter

In general, we find Jeppesen graphics to be more logical and readable than the NOS versions. Part of this is due to the consistent arrangement of elements. Jeppesen, for example, always puts the frequency box in the upper left hand corner of the plate, with the MSA circle immediately to the right. On NOS, the frequencies can be on the left or right, the MSA circle hops around the plan view like a bouncing ball. A minor point, perhaps, but why not keep it consistent? Also, Jeppesen prints the frequencies in larger, bolder type, so they're much easier to read.

Jeppesen's depiction of principal approach features—course, navaids, procedure turns, transitions and step-downs, is much crisper and bolder than NOS's. Part of the better readability is due to the whiter paper Jeppesen uses but the type is generally larger and the symbology bolder, nonetheless.

This clarity carries through to the profile view. On approaches with a stepdown fix, NOS depicts descent profiles with a straight, downward arrow. Jeppesen, by contrast, illustrates the stepdown as it would actually be flown, with a brief level out, followed by a descent further along the track. One other important item, the missed approach procedure, is given in the profile view on NOS plates. Jeppesen puts the missed in its own box, where it's easier to read.

Of course, sometimes Jeppesen's attention to detail and bold type goes too far. When it comes to really cluttered procedures, NOS's spare detailing and smaller type actually improves clarity. This is particularly true on inherently dense charts like SIDs and STARs.

On ordinary approaches, we find that minimums are expressed about equally well in both systems. However, where dual minimums exist, such as DME credit on a VOR approach or remote altimeter minimums, Jeppesen tends to stack the data into an unreadable jumble in the lower right hand corner of the plate. Score one for NOS here. We do like Jeppesen's method of including the inoperative component table right in the minimums box, however. It saves looking it up in the front of the NOS booklet.

Airport data

NOS charts include an airport landing diagram to the right of the minimums box. While this is useful for forming a mental picture of what to expect when you break out at minimums, that's about all it's good for. We find the landing diagram to be far too small to aid in taxiing.

For major airports, NOS provides an airport layout diagram, complete with labeled taxiways and inset details. These are fine, as far as they go. But many mid-sized airports simply aren't covered.

Jeppesen, on the other hand, provides a full-sized airport diagram on the back of the primary plate for that airport, no matter how small the airport. The diagram includes such nice-to-know details as exact runway alignments, and locations of the windsock, beacon and trees off the ends of the runways.

Runway lighting is depicted and explained in a table beneath the diagram. This attention to detail is convenient when landing at night at an unfamiliar airport in rotten weather.

The back of Jeppesen plates includes other data that, as we mentioned earlier, you have to rifle through the NOS booklet to locate. This includes IFR take-off minimums and departure procedures and alternate minimums. Having these all in one place simplifies flight planning. One item Jeppesen has that NOS doesn't is an RNAV waypoint for the airport, from the closest VOR.

Revisions

Now, for the ugly part: revisions. Here, NOS clearly has the better system. Subscribers simply receive new booklets and charts every 56 days and they toss (or recycle...it's newsprint, after all) the old ones. Every 28 days, the mid-cycle Change Notice arrives, announcing major changes and amendments. What could be easier?

In exchange for the convenience of easy updating, NOS subscribers are supposed to consult both the Change Notice and the aforementioned printed notams. This should be done during flight planning or, at the very least, before launching and flying an approach. And as we've said before, don't count on FSS for the notams. Unless you ask, they won't tell you about printed notams.

Jeppesen subscribers face the fortnightly tyranny of hand-inserted revisions. Every two weeks, like clockwork, another brown envelope arrives; some are fat with revisions, some have just a few or perhaps new enroute charts, which are simply inserted into the appropriate wallets in the binder.

Realizing that all this paper shuffling can lead to mistakes, at the end of the year Jeppesen sends a checklist. You're supposed to review all your binders against the list, in search of missing or incorrect charts, which Jeppesen will then replace. Running the checklist is tedious beyond reason and we doubt many pilots do it. (Checking the Northeast, which fills two 2-inch binders, takes the better part of a day.)

Over the years, Jeppesen has tried to ease the pain of revising but for most pilots, there's simply no way around it. If you want accurate data without looking in three sources, you've got to bite the bullet and insert the revisions. Most die-hard Jeppesen subscribers have learned that it's best to insert the revisions the instant they arrive.

Again, we note that Jeppesen has their own "throwaway" service: A few years ago, Jeppesen introduced Q-service, which provides some relief from the update nuisance, but at considerable cost. Q-service subscribers get new binder contents every 16 weeks for the area coverage they've ordered. Between 16-week cycles, subscribers are sent a revision every two weeks, which they file in a separate binder. At the end of the cycle, contents and revisions are tossed out and the process starts over.

There's no insertion of individual plates, as with a standard subscription. All the pilot need do is check the revisions binder for changes affecting his or her route. Q-service nearly doubles the cost of a regular subscription. Full U.S. Q, for instance, is $745, versus $385 for a regular subscription. Typical regional coverage is between $250 and $300, putting it far above NOS.

Jeppesen offers other speciality services as well, including high-performance service featuring only airports with runways longer than 4000 feet, trip kits and the J-Aid. Trip kits, available piecemeal to subscribers and non-subscribers, consist of charts and plates for a full region, such as the northeast or Great Lakes areas. You get the entire contents for the area you'll be flying into, sans revisions. Each trip kit is issued with a 30-day limit but caution is advised: if you happen to buy the kit close to the revision date, you might not have the most up-to-date charts. Check with Jeppesen just before departure. We'll take a closer look at trip kits in a later chapter.

The J-Aid, available separately by subscription even if you don't take Jepps charts, is a combination FAR/AIM and airport directory. It fits into a single two-inch binder and is revised about 13 times a year.

So, which one?

Setting aside the issue of cost for a moment, we think either plate system is more than adequate for safe IFR flying. If you prefer NOS, however, we think it's absolutely essential that you also subscribe, not buy them individually. In addition, you should also subscribe to the printed notams and learn to read the corrections found both there and in the off-cycle Change Notice. We think that pilots should carry the notams book in the airplane on all IFR flights.

If you're looking for the best value, we believe Jeppesen offers the better deal, without question. The plates are more readable and have more useful information than do NOS products. Jeppesen's customer service gets raves from our readers and although the revision process is a pain, if you do it according to the book, you'll be assured of having accurate, up-to-date information in a single publication. All things considered, we think that's the best way to go.

Read just about any commercial aviation magazine and you just can't miss the ads: incredibly dense type expounding the virtues of Air Chart Systems over

Jeppesen and NOS, punctuated by postage-stamp sized photos of the likes of Bob Hoover and Burt Rutan.

The ads are different, just like the product. It's one you either love or you hate; it certainly has its virtues, but there are an awful lot of drawbacks, too.

Among its virtues are its unique update system and its spiral-bound book format.

Among its drawbacks are its unique update system and its spiral-bound book format.

This is not a contradiction: Rather, it's an illustration of the compromises made in the creation of the Air Chart Systems product.

The update system eliminates the tedium of Jepp updates and the waste of NOS throwaways, but it means that before you fly (or during a flight if you get an unexpected route change) you need to root around to see if anything has changed on your charts, then mark them up.

The bound atlas format puts a lot of information in a compact, easily handled collection, but that information was originally printed on fold-out charts in several colors, and it loses something in the translation to the pages of a book.

Air Chart Systems

For most instrument pilots, the choice of chart systems is generally limited to the two major chartmakers: Uncle Sam (NOS) or Jeppesen. But a third option is available, one that's been around for a long time— the Sky Prints atlases from Air Chart Systems.

The idea behind Sky Prints is to provide the lowest-cost chart system available, and that it is. However, the execution is something that you either love or you hate. There are some good ideas here—but the presentation may not be to your liking.

The Sky Prints atlas first came out in 1962. Since then, the original atlas has grown into a variety of books and services, organized so that a pilot can pick and choose those that fit his or her needs. The man who came up with the idea, Howie Keefe, is still in charge of the company.

Basically, what Keefe does is to repackage public-domain NOS material into a form more convenient for users, so in many ways his product has some of the same strengths and weaknesses as NOS charts do. To that selection, he adds some of his own unique products.

What you get

The ACS product line at present consists of four atlases, NOS approach plates that have been bound in plastic loose-leaf rings and which include SIDs and STARS, IFR enroute charts and an update service. Here's a summary:

• **VFR Enroute Atlas**—This contains the original Sky Prints VFR charts, which are unique. It also has a full set of WAC charts that have been reduced to 80 percent of their original size and which are printed in a single color. ACS calls these "GRACs" for Ground Reference Aviation Charts.

• **IFR Atlas**—This contains a full set of NOS low-altitude enroute charts and area charts. They've been cut up to fit the atlas' 11-inch square format, which is roughly the size of two panels of a folded NOS enroute chart.

• **Terminal Atlas**—Contains a set of airport diagrams lifted from the NOS approach plates and a full set of VFR terminal charts (again, printed in one color).

• **Loran/GPS Navigator Atlas**—Formerly a small book, this atlas is now an 11-by-11-inch square wirebound book like the other atlasess, this contains a set of selected Sky Prints VFR Enroute charts, lat/lon coordinates for fixes, a location identifier cross-reference, and listings of tower, Flight Service and Center frequencies.

Each of the books is also chock-full of other stuff. The VFR Atlas has, starting from the front, directions, a well-done proprietary airport directory with frequencies and names, a display of all the communications panels from the NOS enroute charts (redundant, since there's already a directory, but occasionally helpful in locating an airport on the chart), lots of excerpts from the AIM, a mileage chart, chart legends, another proprietary list (this one with lat/lon coordinates of all the VORs) followed by one for NDBs, a listing of commercial broadcast stations, followed by the charts. The book covers the entire lower 48 states.

In detail
The original Sky Prints VFR charts are a kind of enroute chart intended for VFR pilots. They're similar to IFR enroute charts in that they don't show much terrain, only navaids, airports, coastlines and airspace features like Victor airways and restricted areas. While, strictly speaking, the VFR Atlas is not intended for instrument pilots, it is an unusual and interesting product that can prove useful and so bears examination.

There's also a unique feature that's handy for VOR-to-VOR navigation. There are direct lines with ranges and bearings drawn from every VOR to all its neighbors.

The information is presented rather differently than it is on NOS charts. For example, the VOR name, Morse, identifier and frequency are all printed inside the VOR compass rose, rather than floating off to one side in a box.

Each chart also has a place to record airport names and frequencies, a reference map of the U.S., a chart of VORs with their associated Flight Service Stations and the frequencies for each, and a Center frequency map. We particularly like the FSS frequency chart. It's much better than trying to find the FSS name above the frequency box for the VOR, the way it is presented on NOS charts.

With the exception of certain lists, the Sky Prints VFR charts are the only product Air Systems actually creates. Everything else is lifted out of NOS publications and reorganized.

The GRAC charts are next—they don't have the extra features of the VFR Enroute charts. All they are is reduced WAC charts, cut up to fit the book and printed in a single color.

The next book, the IFR Atlas, is similar to the GRAC chart package— each page is a portion of an NOS enroute chart, printed in a single color. They're presented full-size, and cut to fit the book. There are overlaps, so nothing gets lost in the binding. A typical chart, like L-25, takes up eight pages. The IFR Atlas also has a VOR directory and communications panels from the NOS charts. This is the product that would be of most interest to instrument pilots.

The Terminal Atlas has, again, an airport directory, this one with a cross-reference, followed by airport diagrams. These are of the same utility as NOS approach plate diagrams (that is, after all, what they are). In other words, they show you what the field looks like from above and information about it, but not things like taxiway IDs or surrounding terrain details as Jepp charts do. As we noted earlier in the chapter, we like the Jepp treatment much better.

Then come terminal charts, and another pair of proprietary directories—one listing Mode-C veil-exempted airports, and the other a list of localizers and compass locators.

The last atlas, the Loran/GPS Navigator Atlas, is similar to the VFR Enroute Atlas except that it doesn't have GRAC charts, substituting information that is of more interest to those with loran or GPS. Its purpose is to "keep you 'VOR-oriented' in case of lapses in your loran signal." It has the VOR coordinate directory, NDB listing, and airport directory as well.

To Keefe's credit, the approach plate books he's been selling for years are exactly what NOS will be selling when the May '94 changes occur. Formerly, Keefe would slice the binding off the book, drill holes and supply looseleaf rings.

Costs

These charts are nothing if not inexpensive. The works for the entire U.S. costs $299 at present, including a year's update service. Substituting standard approach plates for the ring-bound version cuts $25 from the cost. Various other combinations apply to smaller orders.

That's a pretty good deal, since there's a pile of information here. However, the savings aren't quite so impressive when one takes a look at a more typical IFR order.

To narrow the selection down a bit to just the IFR Atlas (equivalent to full-U.S. NOS enroute service) and the approach plates, the cost is that of the approach plates plus $75.

A full set of approach plates with one year of updates goes for $155, or $125 if standard-issue bound charts are desired. Individual regions can also be ordered.

Net for the full U.S. is $230. For a typical area like the Northeast, it's $50 for the ring-bound plates plus $75 for the atlas, for a total of $125 including the update for a year.

Normally, both the atlas and approach plates will be replaced with a fresh set each year, so the $125 figure is a fair estimate for the annual cost of regional coverage. This compares pretty directly to the current annual Jepp subscription cost of $135 (using our example of the Northeast), though of course there's the previously mentioned startup cost associated with the Jepp service.

The update service alone costs $30 for enroute, $40 for approach, or $60 for both. It can be used by NOS customers who don't want to throw away their charts and plates every 56 days. Going that route instead of buying the IFR atlas really does save a lot of money. Again using the Northeast example, the area is covered by three approach plate books and four enroute charts. At $3 per chart and $3.50 per approach plate book, that's $22.50 to start up, plus $60 for the update service for a total of $82.50 annually.

Unique updates

Perhaps the most interesting thing about the ACS way of doing things is the update procedure.

The two prevailing philosophies of keeping charts current are, a) Throw everything out periodically, and replace it with new material. Handle interim changes via notam. (That's NOS.) Or, b) send frequent updates of the parts that change along with notam sheets. (That's Jeppesen.) The debate over which system is better is an old one, and basically it boils down to personal preference.

Howie Keefe has a different idea. Rather than throw away plates and charts that have changed, why not just mark the changes on the existing chart?

Updates to the atlases are sent out on the normal NOS cycle, every 56 days. It lists chart changes alphabetically, by region. The update sheet is cumulative for about a year, so there's no need to keep old updates around—each subsequent update includes all the changes found on previous updates. Every March a new set of atlases is published and the process begins again.

Nor is it necessary to go through and actually mark the updated information when it comes in. Instead, you make updating the information part of your preflight procedure. You check to see if any of the airways you're planning to use appear on the update, and if so you scribble the changes on the appropriate page of the atlas. The chart you need is now current, and away you go.

The problem with this is that in the real world ATC seemingly never lets you use the airway you want to. If they throw you a curve and send you off in an unexpected direction you now have to dig in your flight bag for the update sheet to see if anything has changed on your new route.

The way around this is to update all the routes you're likely to encounter on a flight, but that begins to get away from ACS's much-touted simplicity and convenience. Plus you need to remember which changes you made and which you didn't.

The process for approach plates is similar, but the changes are mailed out every six weeks instead. Many of these changes are published before their effective dates, so it's important to check and make sure the altered information isn't used too soon.

Interestingly, the update service can be used to make life with Jepp charts easier. Jeppesen sends out bi-weekly updates, and every customer knows the "joy" of grinding through those binders, replacing approach plates (especially if they've been allowed to accumulate).

The idea is you make sure the chart is current as of the start date of the update sheets, which you keep on file, along with the Jeppesen updates. Check each sheet for a given airport, and either mark the change or pull the new plate from the pile of update envelopes as needed.

The good and the bad

As innovative as the Sky Prints VFR charts are, we find that they have too many drawbacks to be useful. One of these is crowded information; in a congested area there's so much surprinting and colliding type that it's virtually impossible to read the chart.

Our other gripe is with the single ink color, particularly on reproductions of what were four-color VFR charts designed to be read in those four colors. Making them one color means that mountain shading is all dark blue, as are roads, rivers, town boundaries, power lines, airport symbols, lat/lon lines...you get the idea. Howie Keefe told us that these are rough maps intended to tell the pilot things like which side of a river the airport is on. To tell the truth, we had trouble distinguishing the river from a road in the first place.

Worse, the GRAC charts are only 80% of the size of a WAC chart, which is already at too large a scale to be really useful for close-in navigation.

The four-color problem extends to the Terminal Atlas. Terminal charts, too, are meant to be seen in color.

Fortunately for the IFR pilot, the IFR atlas is much easier to deal with than the VFR products. That's because the charts are full-size reproductions of charts that don't rely so heavily on color. The type isn't nearly as crowded, and they're just as easy (or difficult, depending on your point of view) to read as NOS charts are.

That doesn't mean they're flawless. Since each chart is cut up, inevitably there are going to be some things near the edge (like frequency boxes) that wind up on the wrong map. Also, if you aren't flying in the right direction, you might find yourself hunting for the right page as you go from one part of the map to another. For example, the bottom part of chart L25, panel A isn't on the next page—it's located four pages away.

Still, the book is a handy size and doesn't become a paper octopus like a normal NOS chart will when unfolded.

Conclusion

For some pilots, particularly those who are less active, the ACS system makes more sense than Jepp or NOS. Others use a combination of bits and pieces of the various systems, seeking to strike a balance between cost, utility and convenience.

One last word about the three systems: It's not necessary to spring for the full subscription to check them out. Jeppesen will send you a sample of their product for free, the local NOS chart and plate book will cost you all of $6.95, and ACS offers a two-month money-back guarantee. So it's a simple thing to get a hands-on trial of the three systems.

Pilots' Preferences

A couple of years ago IFR *magazine published a survey of its readers asking which of the two major chart systems—Jepp or NOS—they preferred.*
The results, in a way, were not surprising: opinion was pretty much evenly divided. There was a surprising result, however—low time pilots seemed to favor Jeppesen.

Jepp or NOS: The Survey Says...

A few years ago, we asked *IFR* readers to tell us which chart and plate system they preferred, the government's NOS products or Jeppesen's well-known Airway Manual service. By the time the responses began to taper off, our tally showed that *IFR* readers are dead even on the question of which system is better; exactly half prefer Jeppesen, half use NOS. A small percentage use both, either because an employer foots the bill or because, as one reader put it, it's nice to have all the bases covered when you're messing around in weather.

Among the readers who sent in survey forms, we counted all manner of instrument pilots, from 130-hour beginners to multi-thousand hour retired airline and military types with lots of instructors and serious business pilots in between. With one exception, the even preference held true among all pilot groups. One surprise: We had expected the professionals to overwhelmingly favor Jeppesen. In fact, according to our survey, they seemed to favor NOS.

Another pattern we found somewhat surprising is that low-time pilots seem to strongly prefer Jeppesen, the mid-timers prefer NOS and the mega-high-timers (more than 10,000 hours) again favor Jeppesen.

Why? We're not sure but as this saga unfolds, we'll be happy to speculate.

Who are these people?

In our survey form we asked readers to tell us which system they used and to provide some general comments on likes and dislikes. We also asked for some background information, including total hours flown and type of flying done; commercial, business, instruction, recreational. We received 358 responses from *IFR* readers plus another 75 from users of Howie Keefe's Air Chart systems, following Keefe's publication of our survey form in his revision letter.

Since the survey was designed to look only at Jepp vs. NOS, we won't examine the ACS responses here. But there was one response that illustrates the way most ACS users felt: "If you like prestige, buy Jepps; if you like paper, buy NOS; but if you like a no-nonsense updating system, buy Air Charts."

Our tally suggests that IFR readers are, on average, relatively experienced pilots who tend to fly on business missions. The average total time of those who responded was 2400 hours. Half—51 percent—described themselves as business pilots, 24 percent fly for recreation only, 10 percent are instructors and 8 percent are airline or professional GA pilots.

Among the group as a whole, 48 percent used NOS, 47 percent used Jeppesen, a difference that's too trivial to imply a preference. Five percent use both Jeppesen and NOS or its cousin, DOD FLIP charts. This group includes a lot of very experienced pilots who are well poised to compare the two systems.

"I pay for NOS myself but use Jepps when flying as a starboard lookout on a local corporate twin," wrote Charles Bolan, a 5000-hour ex-Navy and corporate pilot from Pennsylvania. Like many who've tried both, Bolan can distill the pros and cons of each to one sentence: "NOS has the best update system but Jepps charts are easier to handle, if you don't drop them in the midst of chaos."

Even Steven

We expected those occupying the low end of the aviation food chain—instructors, to be blunt—to prefer NOS, since it's cheaper and it's the system upon which the written exams are based. These assumptions proved wrong, too. If anything, the instructors preferred Jeppesen by a narrow margin, 51 percent versus 48 percent. One reason for this might be that IFR tends to attract older instructors who don't depend on teaching for an income. (We'll admit we're hard to afford on an instructor's slave wages.)

Similarly, among the business pilots, the split is again nearly even but favoring Jeppesen slightly: 49 percent use Jeppesen versus 46 percent for NOS. Readers identifying themselves as commercial pilots showed a noticeable preference for NOS, 50 percent compared to 39 percent for Jeppesen. Why? We haven't a clue. We speculate that the decision may be cost driven. Some NOS users reason that they save money by buying charts and plates as needed but as we said in the last chapter, buying piecemeal increases the chances of missing the Change Notice and NOS's occasional special notices.

We were encouraged, however, that three out of four NOS users said they do subscribe rather than buying their charts over the counter. Less encouraging was the apparent confusion over the government's Notices to Airmen book, which are issued every two weeks and contain important revision data. NOS considers these an indispensable part of its charting system and even Jeppesen recommends that its users subscribe.

We weren't at all surprised to learn that very few pilots actually take this advice. Among the NOS users, only one in ten got printed notams. That percentage doesn't vary much by pilot groups or hours, although the commercial pilots and high timers (5000 hours or more) did seem to subscribe in somewhat higher numbers.

One pilot summed up the printed notams situation with this confused question: "Why should I subscribe? I get notams from FSS and DUAT." As we said in the August issue, many users just don't understand what they're missing.

Low timers versus graybeards

We were curious to see if pilot experience had any bearing on chart preference so we sorted our data into low-time pilots (fewer than 500 hours), high-time pilots (more than 5000) and mega-time, 10,000 hours or more.

One surprise to us is the large percentage of Jeppesen fans among the low-time pilots. Sixty percent of the 58 pilots with fewer than 500 hours favored Jeppesen. In our experience, many new instrument pilots start out with NOS plates because they're cheaper and because that's what many instructors recommend. We've heard quite a few pilots pledge to switch to Jeppesen once they've earned the rating and evidently, quite a few are doing just that.

Among the high-time group, the preference was just the reverse. Forty percent said they used Jeppesen versus 50 percent for NOS and quite a few of the NOS users had defected from Jeppesen. Why? They just got tired of the revisions.

"I used Jeppesen for 15 years but the page replacement problem finally got me down. There's a risk of error, too," wrote one pilot from Long Island.

Curiously, the mega-timers seem to share the same enthusiasm for Jeppesen expressed by the neophytes. Almost 2/3 of them—62 percent versus 23 percent—said they used Jeppesen.

By the way, the great majority of our readers—70 percent—have between 500 and 5000 hours. In that group, NOS and Jeppesen again finished in a dead heat.

Gripes and groans

Of course, no matter how committed to one system or another, pilots do have beefs about both systems and, after all, we did ask.

Jeppesen users seem to have three main complaints: Revisions, revisions and revisions. To that list, some add a fourth gripe; the annual checklist that's supposed to assure that the revisions were done properly. This is a particularly acute problem for pilots who take several regions or entire U.S. coverage.

"With a guy assigned to this job, we are still always behind," wrote the director of operations for a Pennsylvania charter outfit.

A number of pilots reported that they suffer the revisions only because they prefer Jeppesen's looseleaf format, which is generally easier to handle than the NOS bound booklets.

"Jepps is an absolute inconvenience," wrote a 500-hour New York based pilot. "I use it only because NOS is so cumbersome. If NOS had looseleaf, I'd switch immediately."

Many Jeppesen users are also unhappy that they have to subscribe to entire regions, rather than individual states and the higher cost of Jeppesen products over NOS is a leading complaint, too.

"I think many more pilots could enjoy the benefits of Jepps charts if individual states could be purchased, rather than spending large amounts of money and time updating states they will never fly in," said William Reynolds, a CFII from Port Orange, Fla. Quite a few readers also complained about the thin paper Jeppesen uses for both its plates and its enroute charts. A number said they prefer Jeppesen plates but NOS enroutes because the government charts are printed on heavier paper and are issued every 56 days.

In spite of these complaints, Jeppesen users rave about the company's good customer service. "Personal service! I phoned Jeppesen to report an error. A week later they phoned and sent a letter thanking me," writes L.A. Burton, a 6000-hour pilot from New Jersey.

Then there's plain old sentimentality: "Hey, it was Captain Jeppesen who invented the procedure turn and made up the first charts, right? Why change a good thing," said a pilot from Kansas City, Mo.

NOS notes

Die-hard NOS users are just as loyal to their chart system, although for different reasons. NOS users seem to have a love-hate relationship with the bound booklets. On the one hand, they make revisions a snap. When the new booklets arrive, the old ones are thrown away; instant currency.

On the downside, finding the correct approach in an NOS booklet is a pain and once you do find it, holding the book open to the proper page is a chore.

NOS users have devised a number of techniques to address this problem, including rubber bands, clipboards, stationary clips and custom-made chart holders.

"I tear out the individual plates and put them in Jeppesen's clear plastic plate protectors. I find this method is best for bringing a chart up next to the instruments so I can include it in my scan," writes Stephen Fixx, an instructor from Oberlin, Ohio.

We found that quite a few NOS subscribers had defected from Jeppesen, primarily because of the revision hassle and the cost.

"Let's face it, Jepps does a better job at presenting the most legible and up-to-date charts. They charge for it, too, and it's a time-consuming bore to update," says Charles Gendrich of Lansing, Mich.

"Availability. This is where NOS shines," adds Cliff Richards, a 4200-hour professional pilot from Jackson, Calif. "Because most of my flying is on the west coast, I don't subscribe to Jepps. If I have to travel east, the NOS charts and plates are usually available over the counter."

Other minor points NOS users cited are legends in each approach booklet, an airport landing diagram on the front of each plate, new enroute charts every 56 days and the fact that NOS is more compact than Jeppesen, given equivalent coverage. Some NOS users seem to use government plates as an act of reverse status seeking:

"I've often wondered why amateur pilots use Jeppesen. The answer is snob appeal," wrote an instructor from Wisconsin. One former Navy pilot insists that Jeppesen users are all "airline pilot wannabes."

As we mentioned, some pilots use both systems and a handful mix and match, using NOS plates with Jeppesen enroutes or the other way around.

"Why stick with just one system?" asks an instructor from the midwest. "You can pick the best of both worlds and maybe even save a little money."

Save money? No kidding? We're not so sure you can actually pull that off. As we noted in the last chapter, the costs of the services are pretty high even without attempting to duplicate portions of the service.

And that's what you'd be doing in most cases. For example, our personal preference would be to use the NOS enroutes (particularly now that they've added four-color printing) to our Jeppesen approach plates, which we like better despite the drudgery of updating. All well and good, but you can't subscribe to just the approach plates. (Interestingly, Jepp does allow you to subscribe to enroutes only.)

Likewise, using the idea we presented in the last chapter of bypassing the Jepp update chore by subscribing to ACS's update service increases, not decreases, the cost.

A Visit With Captain Jepp

R egardless of whether you love them or hate them,
the charts published by Jeppesen are a true institu-
tion. In fact, (and many pilots do not know this)
Jepps were the original IFR charts and plates, predating those issued by the
government.

In 1991 we were priveleged to have the opportunity to visit and talk with
Captain Jeppesen himself. We gained a great deal of insight into what went
into those charts so many of us use, and in fact, what went into instrument
flying, itself.

An Interview with E.B. Jeppesen

In the overall scheme of the universe, 60 years doesn't even qualify as
the blink of an eye. It amounts to less than squat; a tiny immeasurable
portion of a nanosecond.

You'd think that events which occurred so recently—the cosmologi-
cal equivalent of a sentence spoken in the last breath—would be
instantly retrievable in some form and in nearly real-time detail. But it
ain't necessarily so, as we've found out repeatedly in our efforts to
chronicle the early days of instrument flight. The modern IFR system
is so reliable that when we launch into IMC, there's little doubt that we
can navigate to our destination and descend out of the clouds to within
sight of a runway. It's easy to forget that a mere 60 years ago, what now
seems commonplace loomed just out of reach.

The gritty details of instrument flying's evolution are scattered
around enough governmental and personal archives to make it all but
impossible to compile an accurate history. Still, one man has managed

to do exactly that, even if that wasn't his intent. That man is Captain Elrey B. Jeppesen.

Jepp is best known as the founder of a company that published the first instrument enroute and approach charts. Few realize, however, that before they could be published, those procedures had to be developed. Jepp did that, too. It's not an exaggeration to say that Jepp invented instrument flying as we know it.

As did many of his generation, Jepp became hooked on flying at a young age, after paying $5 for a ride in a Jenny in 1921. He bought his first airplane—a $500 Jenny—in 1927 and went barnstorming through the western states. When his travels took him to Dallas, Jepp took a job with Fairchild, doing aerial survey work in Louisiana and eventually in Mexico. Later, he signed on with a Portland airmail operator for his first tour as a mail pilot.

He's not sure if his Fairchild experience piqued his interest in chartmaking but by 1930, Jepp had begun to compile detailed notes on the airmail routes he was flying, including fixes along the way and airport diagrams. These notes became the basis for his famous "little

Captain Jepp has a copy of just about every chart he ever made, including the original little black book.

black book" and represented the prototypes for what has become the modern instrument approach procedure.

Jepp and his wife, Nadine, operated the growing chart business from various basements around the country, while Jepp continued his flying career with United Air Lines, the successor to Boeing Air Transport, an early mail and passenger line. Through the war years, Jeppesen & Co. established itself (and it remains) the dominant commercial maker of aeronautical charts. Jepp flew the line with United until 1954 and ran the business full time until 1961, when he sold the company to Times Mirror Co. Jepp was 84 at the time of the interview but apart from a touch of Parkinson's, he hardly shows it; his memory is sharp and true for just the kind of detail for which his charts have become famous. He and Nadine live in Englewood, Colo., a pleasant suburb of Denver.

Jepp had—and still has—a steadfast eye for detail, a virtue that's carried through to the products published by the company that bears his name. Fortunately, Jepp seems to have squirreled away in his basement copies (in some cases, many copies) of every procedure and chart he devised plus boxes of fascinating memorabilia, including the bill of sale for his first airplane, the aforementioned Jenny.

When we visited him in late 1991 to conduct the interview that follows here, Jepp was sorting through his archives, with the assistance of Jeppesen staffers Ralph Latimer and Donna Chandler in preparation for the design a permanent exhibition to be housed at the new Denver airport, whose terminal will be named in honor of Captain Jepp.

The exhibition will include early photographs, enroute and approach charts, plus a representative selection of Captain Jepp's personal records, collected during his remarkable aviation career. It should be a fitting tribute to the man behind it all. We encourage you to seek it out if you have the chance.

—By the late 1920s, you'd done quite a bit of barnstorming and flown with Tex Rankin's Flying Circus out of Portland and that led to a job doing aerial photography for Fairchild. How did you start flying the airmail?

Well, after Fairchild, I'd flown for Varney out of Portland. That was in April 1930. After that, I went with Boeing Air Transport but I didn't fly much. They hadn't any work in those days, just no openings. There were only one or two airplanes going everyday between Oakland and Chicago and that was the transcontinental in those days. That was all single-engine airplanes, the Boeing 40-Bs. And they had an experimental Tri-Motor Boeing they were playing with.

When the Depression came along, I went back with Fairchild up in

St. Paul, flying a run over to Duluth and Eau Claire. Fairchild wanted me to go back to New York and I said no, I'm going to Cheyenne and try to get my airmail job back. And I got hired on.

—With the airmail contracts, there must have been a lot of pressure to fly, no matter what the weather.
Well, there was. You didn't have very much in the way of weather reporting. They had a few farmers around some of the towns and they'd spot for us and maybe call the sheriff's department with a report. I remember up near Laramie, they stationed a crew about 50 or 60 miles north of the airport to catch those cold fronts coming down into Cheyenne. That worked pretty well. Most of time, though, we didn't know what to expect.

Whether to go or not was pretty much up to the pilot. If you didn't get the mail through, you might get canned. If you got it through in conditions that were a little too hard, why you might get yourself knocked off. I know back in the early days some of the post office people used to say we had to fly, no matter what. One of the pilots, Ham Lee, wouldn't go, so they fired him. They picked the next pilot and told him to go and the fellow said if Ham won't go, I'm not gonna go. I guess if we hadn't straightened it out, they'd have fired us all.

—At that time—you said about 1930—there weren't any navigation aids, other than the lighted airway beacons. Were you able to fly the 40-B on instruments?
I did a little of it. But I'd say 80 percent of the pilots didn't fly any instruments at all. You weren't really equipped to fly instruments. The 40-B had a turn and bank, a compass and an altimeter and that's about it. At first, there was no electrical system. The gyro (turn and bank) was a vacuum driven deal with that thing sticking out the side of the airplane. It would ice up once in a while and of course, it wouldn't do you a damn bit of good. Then you'd get a little ice on the wings and those wires would start to vibrate and they'd pop just like a rifle. It kind of shook you up a little bit.

The Tri-Motor Boeing was a little better. It had a horizon in it but you couldn't rely on it. You couldn't use it for a straight-ahead climb. You'd bring the nose up and this thing would only hold the pitch for three or four minutes and then it would sink down. Can you imagine trying to fly instruments with something like that?

—It sounds like flying in IMC was possible but there must have been no way to navigate, other than dead reckoning.

Thanks to his talent for recording and preserving information, Jepp's original notebook is in pristine condition. It contains notes on landing fields, pilotage and dead reckoning and early low-frequency radio ranges.

That's about right. Sometimes you could get up on top of a low overcast or a fogged-in condition and fly over that. If you got stuck on top, you'd better find a hole or find someplace you could let down.

Down in Mexico, with Fairchild, I used to fly on instruments between Mexico City and Tampico. Of course, I didn't have to worry about the letdown because I had the whole Gulf to shoot at. I'd just fly over the inland until I was pretty certain I was over the flat area or the water. If I was over the water, I'd just come back and run a landfall, then up the coast up to Tampico.

—How about in the Rockies, where you did most your flying. It must have been doubly difficult to navigate near high terrain.
Actually, I think weather flying was a little easier over the mountains than it was over there in Cleveland and New York. Out here, you've got all the mountains and valleys and you could usually find a place to get down. Over there, as I understand it, everything would get fogged in for

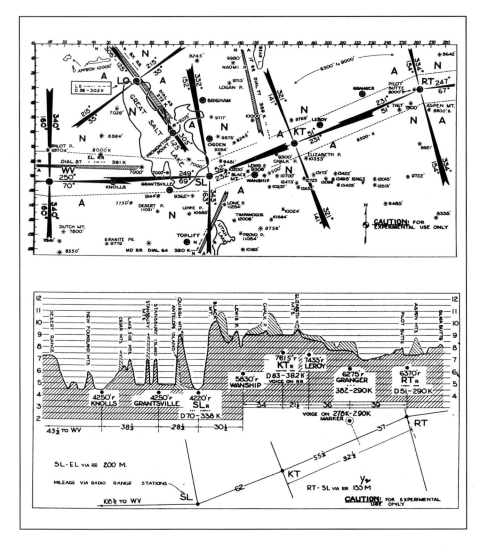

Early enroute charts from a Jeppesen Airway Manual. These are 80 percent of full size. By the late 1930s, coast-to-coast coverage was available.

miles. Of course, I never flew out east.

Fellows going into Portland, for instance, they'd line up with Mount St. Helens and Mount Hood poking up through the clouds and sort of spiral down. But you had to have pretty good ceilings to do that.

—When did you begin to realize that commercial aviation would have to be built around instrument flying?

The first Airway Manual

Jeppesen's first commercial instrument charts were primarily enroute aids based on four-legged, low-frequency radio ranges. These charts—reproduced at left—depict the major transcontinental airway between Rock Springs, Wyo. and Salt Lake, circa late 1930s. In those days, a pilot could carry Jeppesen's complete U.S. coverage in a coat pocket and still have room for a wallet and comb. Today, it takes eight 2-in. binders to cover the country.

The charts shown on the opposite page are reproduced as they would have appeared in the early Airway Manual, with a profile view on top and a plan view depicting major navigation aids on the bottom. Dashed lines on the plan view represent the width of the airway, which is given as about 20 miles on this segment.

Before ATC came into the picture in 1936, pilots were on their own to determine altitude, although hemispheric rules existed, as they do today for most IFR traffic. The dark cross-hatched area in the profile view gives peak elevations along the airway; the lighter cross-hatching depicts highest elevations at a specified maximum distance beyond the airway centerline, probably about 20 miles on this chart.

By the early 1940s, the Airway Manual had evolved to its present 7 1/2 in. by 9 in. format. The ring-bound enroute chart, which many pilots found quite convenient, was retained until 1951, when the first folded enroute chart was produced.

Today, the Rock Springs to Salt Lake segment is covered by one low-altitude chart (US LO 7), the US HI 1 and an RNAV chart. Most of the original airports and fixes—including Granger, Wyo.—have long since been dropped from the charts.

I'm not sure I ever really did realize it. You know, at the time I started flying, I was just a kid. These older guys had been flying for eight or ten years. I didn't really think much about a system or publishing it. I really did it just to save my own hide.

I started making notes and trying to remember as much as I could by getting it down in writing so I could rehearse it, then I'd have it some day when I really needed it. It's hard to believe now but back then, we didn't have much to go on at all. You'd come chugging along there at night...there aren't any lights to speak of around the airport except for a beacon...you hoped.

The fact that I was so young helped some, I guess. One day they'd send me on a route in this direction, and one day another. Maybe the next day somebody would get hurt or something, that happened a lot, you know. Well, they'd say send Jepp over there and let him fly the route for a few weeks instead of sending a family man. All he's got is a suitcase. And that's about right, too, that's all I had.

—Is it true that some of the veteran pilots weren't too enthusiastic about IFR flying?
Looking back, it's hard to believe but a lot of pilots, a lot of the old timers never did adapt to IFR. I remember once, after the Tri-Motor Boeing came in, this was about 1930. Well, anyway, the government decided we all had to have a radio license. So they picked us up in a Tri-Motor and we all went to San Francisco to get a radio license. We had eight or nine pilots on that Boeing, from Cheyenne and Salt Lake.

We landed in Sacramento, trying to get to Reno. We would fly up the hills, down the canyons and all around, looking for holes. Finally, we got back on the ground in Sacramento about 5 o'clock.

Well, I guess we got to drinking a little bit and I casually mentioned that one of these days, we were going to be able to fly through that weather or fly up over it. Old Ray Little, God, he got mad. He started poking me in the chest with his two fingers and he says, "I know every rock, every river and every pebble on that mountain between here and Reno," he says, "and I tell you, we'll never do that."

I finally snuck away. But Ray called the chief pilot and said "You better watch that guy Jeppesen. He's got some strange ideas about flying."

But not everyone was like that. Some of the old timers turned out to be pretty fair instrument pilots. They went on to fly the Boeing 247 and the DC-3.

—When did radio navigation first make it practical to fly from one point to another?
They were putting in the radio beams, the old four-legged radio ranges, as early as 1930, I think. The stations were kind of spotted across the country, not really what you could call an airway system, nothing at all like you have now.

But they weren't using them. They had no procedures for them, no charts, just nothing at all. In fact, they never even published the frequencies for quite a long while. You couldn't even find out where the legs ran. I guess the government didn't want us fooling around with them.

—But you did anyway?
Oh, yes. I used to take the chief pilot's airplane, the 40-B that he checked everybody out in, and go over to work letdown procedures. We had dug some of the frequencies out of the Department of Commerce by then. Anyway, I'd fly over to Laramie or Rock Springs and various places trying to figure out how you could use the ranges to get down under a ceiling of maybe 500 or 600 feet.

I'd do it in visual conditions, of course, and then I'd write it all down so I'd have it for a bad night. I probably worked out most of the procedures between Chicago and Oakland that way, between 1932 or 1933. Lots of other fellows, the younger ones, were trying to do the same thing. And they'd pass the information on to me.

—Did you just go to each airport and work things out on the fly or did you have some government topo charts to work from?
I never did see any government charts in those days. We didn't have much of anything, really. Rand McNally wasn't making aeronautical charts. Guys going cross country kind of felt their way along the highways or maybe a river or railroad. You were really on your own.

So for the letdowns, I'd do most of it visually. I'd go out and fly a five or ten mile circle and take a look. Then I'd figure that the logical way to do it was to come in on this beam or that beam, get the cone of silence and turn ten degrees this way or thirty that way. Then I'd figure out a descent point where you could go down to maybe 300 feet. And then I'd figure 30 seconds later or a minute, you'd have to pull up if you didn't see the airport.

—How about elevations and distances and all the other technical detail that goes into plates and charts?
Even then, the survey information wasn't very good. You'd be surprised. There was one peak out of east of Salt Lake, they had no elevation on it. It's about 9200 feet but they had no elevation.

Later on, during the war, when the Japanese were moving into the Aleutian Islands, they locked us up down here in the bank building and had us make instrument charts for Alaska. Some of those mountains had seven elevations for the same one and they'd vary two or three thousand feet. I'd just take the highest one and put a plus or minus on it, which meant the elevation was uncertain.

The best information I got was from the engineering department at the Union Pacific in Omaha. But a lot of it, why, I'd just go out and get myself. I'd maybe drive or fly out there and try to get an elevation at the base and an estimate for the top. Some of them I climbed up with an altimeter, which seemed like a pretty antiquated way of doing it but it was all I had.

I'd get a lot from pilots, too. I used to send these things out (a form with courses, elevations, distances, etc.). The pilot could sketch in the information then we'd have to go back and survey it.

—What sort of minimums did you have on those early approaches and how did you determine them?
Oh, if you got a good clear signal, you could go down to 200 feet. Maybe a little lower than that. But we really didn't have any minimums the way you do now. It was really up to the pilot. The procedures weren't standard in those days.

—You mean everyone would fly an approach differently?
Yes, that's right. You see, in 1930 and 1931, we had no air traffic control of any kind. We did have radios so we could call down to the dispatcher and tell him where we were and maybe that we were starting our procedure at Salt Lake, but that was it.

In fact, that's an interesting point. When I first started selling the Airway Manual, every airline had their own procedures. United, Western, American, and so on. I'd go down and see the chief pilot and he'd say "Jepp, what can you do for me?" And I'd explain the Airway Manual. Then he'd say something like "Well, if I want to change the altitude of this procedure turn or some such, I can just call in the office girl there and have her do it and make a bunch of mimeograph copies for the pilots."

So what I did was to set up a tailored service and a standard service. I could see that it was going to become standard some day, with all of the traffic we were getting. But when I came to sell you a manual, I'd tailor it just the way you wanted it. Before too long, the letdowns were standard and I didn't have to do as much tailoring.

—Your early Airway Manuals show airways and approaches built entirely on the low-frequency ranges. What was it like to fly the ranges?
We did pretty well with it but at the time, it was kind of an uncertain thing. You'd listen for an A on one side of the course and N on the other, then a more or less constant tone between. Pretty soon, it'd just fade out for a little while and you'd pick it up on the other side and you'd know you had gone over the station, through the cone of silence. Lots of times, though, you couldn't hear much because of snow static and so forth. Ice, too. One night I lost most of my antennas down there in the Laramie

Valley. They iced up and broke off. I didn't hear anything at all until all the way past Elko. I just climbed up to 14,000 feet. I came out three or four miles north of the airway, past Elko. By then, the clouds were breaking up and I could just start to pick up the lights.

Even in the DC-3, we still had to dead reckon. For instance, you'd come out of Cheyenne and you'd cross this beam and you'd take your time and when you'd cross the next beam, it'd give you some idea of the kind of wind you were bucking, headwind or tailwind.

There was no other way to tell how far out on the range leg you were and that could get confusing. I remember the east leg of the Salt Lake range, you'd fly north and south across it and get 20 or 25 on-course signals because the thing would bounce around between those peaks.

Even when you knew where you were on the approach, it wasn't easy. You had to be careful around those mountains. The manager there at Salt Lake had a phone put in at the far corner of the field to get way from all the noise, then he'd listen for you and give you a position report. "Yeah, I hear you, Jepp, over to the northwest, blurp your engine." At least then you knew you were past the mountains so you'd go back to the range station and work a letdown.

—At the time, were you the only one making charts or were there others too?
Oh, there must have been seven or eight fellows trying to get into the business. They never really got anywhere with it. I've got one of them around here somewhere by a fellow who was a dispatcher at Braniff, I think. He was under a handicap, you know, because he was doing it from the ground. I was doing it from the cockpit.

I never could understand why none of the big companies like Rand McNally got into it. I guess they were making so much money in the road map business they couldn't see aviation coming. I know I was told that every time Rand McNally checked up on me, they thought I was going broke. I guess I had them fooled. I think they thought the government was going to take it over. The government eventually did start making charts but not until about 1938, I think.

—Your first published charts were in these small binders, about the size of the original black book?
Yes. I had been talking to United Airlines...I flew for United, you know...and they wanted the manuals so I printed up 50 procedures and let them have those. I just sort of kept enlarging it from there. I had the whole United States charted like this when the war broke out. Eventually...must have been before the war, we went to the larger size

plates that you have now. Fred Kelly at Western wanted the whole thing in the small size so it would fit in a coat pocket. He paid the printing bill. But they were too small to read so we went back to the larger size.

When Nadine and I got married in 1936, we ran the chart business out of the basement at Salt Lake. At that time, getting the charts out on time wasn't easy. I'd go see a printer and he'd say "Well, I can get that out in ten days." Of course, I needed it in two hours.

I didn't know anything about printing but I learned quick. Learned about paper, too. Grain, crackle, burst, that sort of thing. Over the years, we've done a lot of things that you wouldn't think would make a difference. During the war, I had to go see Forrestal (Secretary of the Navy) to get a barrel of titanium so the paper would be opaque enough to print on both sides without showing through.

Look at this binder, with seven rings. It had to have seven because the paper's so light it would rip too easy with fewer rings. Then we put the lock booster on the rings so the binder wouldn't open up and spill everything all over the cockpit. Then we figured out that putting round corners on the plates would keep them from getting dog-eared after a month or two. Little things like that really made a difference, I think.

—Looking back on those early procedures and plates, would you have changed anything if you had all to do over again?
I've wondered about that a lot. If you just woke up and you'd never seen nor heard of an airway system, what would the charts look like? The one I built had the frequency at the top, with the letdown in the middle, and the pull-up down here, then the minimums below that. It hasn't changed in 50-some years. I think it worked out pretty good.

Supplementary Chart Products

The basic, run-of-the-mill enroute chart and approach plate collection isn't the only thing published by the chartmakers. There are other services as well, plus a wide variety of anciliary gadgetry that goes along with it.

In this chapter we'll cover some of the less-esoteric printed matter put out by NOS and Jeppesen (Jeppesen and NOS both have some unusual products in their price lists: if you really need approach plates for places like Kabul, they can supply them). We've already described the full line of Air Charts atlases in the first chapter.

First up is a look at the way the various services handle the occasional need of IFR pilots to fly outside their normal stomping grounds.

Trip Kits

One of the most useful resources on the *IFR* bookshelf is a set of binders filled with Jeppesen's full U.S. coverage. Unfortunately, these plates aren't for navigation; they're an old expired Q-service that a friend of ours sent last year. When travel takes us beyond our normal Jepps coverage, we do what everyone else does: we buy a trip kit.

What to look for in trip kits? We figure currency, convenience and low cost are the prime considerations, although not necessarily in that order. By currency, we mean having the latest data and reducing to a tolerable minimum the chances of getting bitten by a missing or out-of-date plate or chart. True, the vast majority of chart changes are trivial and have little or no effect on the safety of flight. In that sense, there's only a remote chance that flying with stale charts will get you into serious trouble. Nonetheless, it's still prudent to observe the spirit if not the letter of FAR 91.103, the all-available information clause.

Convenience and cost bear on the trip kit consideration in ways that don't necessarily relate to your regular charts. If you've settled on NOS or Jeppesen, you pay the bill and get your charts by subscription. They arrive in the mail on or before the effective date. When a trip takes you beyond your regular coverage, you may need additional charts in a hurry. If you're a big-time procrastinator, that may mean overnight. This service is available but it'll cost you.

Piecemeal from Jeppesen

Anyone who's been pummeled by Jeppesen's relentless revisions knows that the company primarily sells charts by subscription. Until just a few years ago, the only way to get a trip kit from Jeppesen was to subscribe to the service for the region you wanted. These days, Jeppesen will sell trip kits to all comers, an option that gives hard-core NOS users a chance to sample the competition.

Jeppesen divides the country into seven coverage areas: northeast, southeast, south central, Great Lakes, north central, southwest and northwest. For trip kits, these regions can be combined in various ways (entire east or central and east, for example). This saves a few dollars over buying the regions individually.

If you're a Jepp subscriber, a trip kit consists of all of the charts and plates for the specified region, plus area charts (where available) and terminal charts. Not included is the introductory section containing the chart and plate legend and a glossary nor the state section tabs for the plates.

Jeppesen subscribers do get a favorable rate on trip kits. The larger regions cost $51 versus $68 for non-subscribers. The extra charge for non-subscribers goes in part to pay for the introduction and state tabs that subscribers already have. Non-subscribers will also need to buy binders or settle for carrying around their plates bundled up with a rubber band.

Depending on where you live and where your trip happens to be, Jepp trip kits can add up to a sizable piece of change. We subscribe to northeast coverage, for example, but frequently fly to Florida, which is covered by Jeppesen's $51 southeast trip kit. If we ordered at the last minute, as we usually do, it would cost us an additional $15 for rush handling, plus $13 for overnight shipping. Grand total: $79. NOS coverage for the same trip would cost about $20 sent by first-class mail or about $32 tops, for overnight service.

Limited guarantee

Most well-stocked pilot shops carry a good selection of NOS en route charts and plate booklets but you'll never find Jeppesen products sold directly via retail. That's because Jeppesen's stock-in-trade currency depends on revisions mailed to subscribers every two weeks; charts sold retail would be obsolete by the time they hit the shelves.

What about trip kits, then, don't they go stale just as quickly? The answer is yes and for that reason, Jeppesen guarantees a trip kit's currency only on the day it arrives. If the kit is shipped a few days before the next revision cycle, it may be obsolete by the time your trip commences.

In practical terms, we don't see this as a huge safety problem. As we said, most chart changes amend inconsequential details, not major items of earth-shaking importance. We're not condoning the use of out-of-date charts, mind you, we just think it's highly unlikely that you'll motor into the side of a mountain because of a missed chart change.

Don't forget, Jeppesen doesn't revise every chart and plate on the two-week cycle anyway so a trip kit that's officially out of date doesn't turn into a pumpkin at the stroke of the revision cycle. The overwhelming majority of plates in the kit will still be up to date; you'll just have no way of knowing which ones aren't.

As far as currency goes, planning ahead won't help. What matters more is how your trip date relates to the revision date. Jeppesen recommends that pilots order kits at least two weeks prior to the planned trip; they do not guarantee delivery by a definite date. The reason for the sluggish delivery time is that Jeppesen products literally are kits. They have to be assembled by hand from bins containing individual plates and charts, which is what the rush charge covers. If you're in a real hurry, call Jeppesen before 11 a.m. Mountain Time and they'll usually ship overnight.

Jeppesen is the sole source of trip kits. The Chart Doctor service offered by Sporty's Pilot Shop processes Jeppesen's regular subscriptions but the company keeps trip kit sales under its own roof. As part of its trip kit service, Jeppesen now sells NOS sectionals, WACs and terminal charts. Also, if you prefer Jeppesen's en route charts over NOS products, you can buy them separately.

Government charts

NOS's bound booklets lend themselves readily to piecemeal purchase, usually at a fraction of the cost of Jeppesen products. NOS charts and plates are issued every 56 days, in accordance with the airspace cycle. Revisions are communicated in two ways, via a Change Notice booklet issued between the airspace cycles and by notams. The notams that apply to charts appear in two places, on the Service A network that transmits weather data to FSS briefers and DUAT and in the Notices to Airmen booklet published every two weeks by the FAA.

In effect, then, if you have the Change Notice, check notams before every flight (you're supposed to) and subscribe to the biweekly notams publication (the FAA expects that, too), you'll be as current as possible, assuming, of course, you can decode the notam language. (It's not easy.)

There's really no convenient way for a Jeppesen trip kit buyer to stay current in the equivalent way. As part of the standard service, a Jeppesen subscriber receives an edited version of the biweekly notams plus selectively revised plates when changes are serious enough to warrant it. Daily notams do apply equally to Jeppesen products but many amendments are never announced in notams; Jeppesen simply issues a new plate. If you subscribe to Jeppesen coverage for any part of the country, you'll receive notams for the entire U.S. and that helps some. But you won't receive any plate or chart revisions because Jeppesen doesn't update trip kits.

Where to buy

Unlike Jeppesen products, NOS charts and plates are widely retailed. If a local pilot shop has the necessary coverage, it may be easiest to buy locally. NOAA does set maximum prices for its agents but they're free to sell the charts as cheaply as they wish so it pays to shop around, especially if you're buying mail order.

Whatever the source, be sure to buy the Change Notice, too. We also recommend that you subscribe to the aforementioned Notices to Airmen publication, which is available from the Government Printing Office. Having made that pitch, it's only fair to say that very few pilots actually do subscribe to the notam book; in fact, very few understand it, thinking that the notams in the book are the same ones the briefer reads you when you get your weather (they're not).

Again, this is probably of little practical consequence, in part because in 1991 the FAA introduced a new notam called a CCP, for Chart Change Permanent. The CCP notam frees NOS from an FAA-imposed restriction that kept it from issuing new plates to reflect certain kinds of data changes. Before last year, NOS wasn't permitted to chart temporary notams of a permanent nature (only a government could come up with a concept like that). As a result, many NOS plates carried stale or inaccurate data in revision after revision. Pilots were expected to unearth the current data as a correction in the notams booklet. Simply stated, the CCP notam corrects this shortcoming so NOS plates are generally more current and accurate than they used to be.

You can order NOS products directly from the NOAA Distribution

Branch or from one of several mail order outfits, including AOPA, whose members get a small discount. Prices vary enough to justify shopping but more important to the mail order buyer is service. Are the proper charts stocked and can they be shipped quickly, overnight if necessary?

NOAA is marginally the cheapest source of NOS charts, although not necessarily the best, in our view. NOAA charges $3.60 for plate booklets; $3.35 for en route charts. For our Florida trip we needed three plate booklets (SE-1, SE-2 and SE-3) plus four en route charts, which would have brought the total to $24.20. NOAA's standard shipping— UPS ground—is included in the chart price. However, NOAA cautions to allow two weeks for processing and no promises are made on delivery. For a rush order, NOAA doesn't charge extra but requires five to seven days. If you have a Federal Express account number, they'll ship that way but allow at least three days; overnight service isn't available.

If you're an AOPA member, the association will sell you plate booklets for slightly more than NOAA will, and they do offer overnight shipping.

Sporty's charges the same as NOAA, but shipping is extra. All of these vendors also stock sectionals, WACs and terminal charts, which we think are just as important to have as IFR charts.

Sporty's and AOPA both get kudos for good service. Both have toll-free order numbers and although Sporty's is a little more efficient, we don't mind waiting a few minutes on AOPA's line to save a few dollars. NOAA answers the phone well enough but the lack of reliable rush service makes them a non-starter, in our view.

Air Charts alternative

A lesser-known third alternative is Howie Keefe's Air Chart Systems. We discussed these in detail in the first chapter but just to review, Air Charts repackages NOS charts and plates and furnishes mailed updates on a six-week cycle. Rather than individual en route charts, Keefe reproduces the government charts and binds them into spiral-bound atlases. Plate booklets are identical to the NOS version, except they're easier to handle because Keefe offers pilots the option of a booklet whose government-issue gum binding has been clipped off and replaced by a plastic ring binder.

Air Charts promotes its products as being ideal for the pilot who needs IFR chart coverage only occasionally. But for trip kit purposes, Air Charts is an expensive way to go, chiefly because it's all or nothing. For en routes, at least, there's no way to buy regional coverage for an area smaller than half the country. For our Florida trip, we would have to spend $75 for the IFR Atlas covering the entire U.S, plus $30 for the three plate booklets with government-issue gum binding. Shipping would add another $9; UPS overnight would add another $25. That totals to more than $125. We could save $10 by ordering eastern U.S. coverage, in which case Air Charts would provide the standard NOS en route charts instead of the bound atlas. Unfortunately, both the loose charts and the atlas unnecessarily duplicate the northeastern coverage we already have.

One advantage of Air Charts is that the entry price includes a year of updates, so a trip kit remains current for longer than do Jeppesen or NOS products. We can see how this might be an advantage for repeat trips over the course of a year's flying. There is one hitch, though. The atlases are issued in March. If you bought one in February, it'll soon be out of date and the six-week updater won't describe the relevant changes. Howie Keefe tells us that some pilots subscribe to just the updater, using the information provided to freshen a Jeppesen or NOS trip kit.

Conclusion

As we said in the first chapter, we think Jeppesen is the best choice for regular coverage. But we have to concede that the same devotion to regular revisions that make Jeppesen the best bet for subscribers is a distinct liability when it comes to trip kits. Bought on a one-time basis, Jepp charts are expensive and they go stale rather quickly.

NOS charts, on the other hand, are less expensive when bought piecemeal. You can purchase them retail or, if necessary, have them shipped overnight by mail order. We still think Jeppesen's graphic design is far superior to NOS's fuzzy ink on newsprint but for occasional use on trips, it's just not worth three or four times the money.

Sporty's is a good source for NOS products but AOPA offers good deals to its members, which by now must include every man, woman and child who has had so much as a passing thought about airplanes.

While we're still on the subject of charts, it's worth talking about Jeppesen's somewhat unusual RNAV service. Unlike NOS, Jepp's RNAV approach information is sold separately on the premise that not everyone has area navigation. Besides, they get to charge more that way. There is no NOS equivalent for Jepp's RNAV enroutes.

Even if you don't have RNAV, the RNAV enroute charts can prove handy because of their unique features.

It'll be interesting to see what happens as GPS becomes more prevalent and GPS approaches start to come on-line.

Jeppesen's RNAV Service

For those of us who ply the murky skies between Boston and Richmond, venturing a hundred miles inland is like entering IFR Shangri-La. The controllers no longer snarl, our requests are instantly granted with disarming cheerfulness and—best of all—the concept of direct routing is understood and practiced.

You remember direct routing. That's where you file a flight plan defined by fixes that actually lead to your destination. If all goes well, you may even be allowed to turn on course right after takeoff. Good as that sounds, it can be a little disorienting for us city folk. We're accustomed to flying at least 30 miles in the opposite direction before turning on course.

Trust us, though, direct routing is practical, providing you have the necessary equipment (not necessarily RNAV, either), know how to file the flight plan and you're willing to grease the skids a little with ATC. For hard-core off-airways navigators, Jeppesen offers complete RNAV coverage of the U.S., including specialized en route charts and approach plates.

Jeppesen introduced its RNAV service back in the mid-1970s, when rho-theta (phantom VOR) RNAV receivers were finding their way into many cockpits. Even with the popularity of loran and GPS, there's still a lot of RNAV out there and probably will be for the next ten years. That explains why Jeppesen still sells quite a bit of RNAV coverage.

As do its other services, Jeppesen RNAV subscriptions come in two components, each of which can be purchased separately. The service consists of six en route charts, one of which is a full U.S. planning chart, plus all of the RNAV and loran approaches for the U.S. Initial cost for either enroute or approach service is $18: there is no package. A yearly sub costs $50 for the plates, $54 for the enroutes and either can be purchased separately. However, for the plates, if you're in for a penny you're in for a pound; the sub includes every U.S. RNAV approach and there's no way to buy them region by region.

So here's the dilemma: You either carry around an extra binder for the inch-high stack of additional procedures or you pick out the ones that apply to the area you're flying in and insert them in your regular binder. Unless you're flying transcontinental, we recommend the latter.

The plates are standard-issue Jepps but we find two things worth mentioning. Few, if any, have airport diagrams because RNAV approaches are always secondary procedures to airports that already have a conventional approach.

The RNAV planning and navigation charts are unique to Jeppesen; NOS has no equivalent product. The planning chart covers the entire U.S. and is supposed to be used in much the same way as Jeppesen's FP/ LO planing chart. It depicts VORs of all classes, along with MOAs and restricted areas and Center boundaries but, of course, no airways. Class B areas are listed by city but not depicted on the chart so don't even think about using this one for VFR navigation.

The en route charts are in much larger scale and cover the U.S. in sections. Each chart depicts all VORs, Center boundaries with frequencies, Class B and C areas, restricted and prohibited areas and all airports, whether they have an approach or not. VORs with DME capability have extended cardinal radials, which assist in locating waypoints. The chart is divided into grids formed by parallels and meridians. Within each grid is something Jeppesen calls a Grid MORA or Minimum Off-Airways Route Altitude. The Grid MORAs are similar to the minimum altitudes given in the quadrangles on sectional charts. However, unlike sectionals, the published figure does include obstacle clearance. For MORAs of 7000 or less, 1000 feet of terrain clearance is provided; published MORAs greater than 7000 feet allow 2000 feet of obstacle protection.

Included with the en routes is a very thorough legend explaining how RNAV courses should be plotted and filed. The general idea is to draw a direct line between the departure and destination airports, without respect to where the VORs are located. The course line will inevitably cross a number of those extended cardinal radials we mentioned.

To establish a waypoint, simply measure the mileage out from the VOR to the point where the course line intersects the radial. The PV-5 plotter Jeppesen sends with all of its initial subscriptions performs this task handily. If the course doesn't intersect a cardinal radial, you can use the plotter to extend a convenient radial.

The accepted convention for defining waypoints is radial/distance. For example, if the desired waypoint is on the 180-degree radial, 12 miles from the CMK VOR, the waypoint is CMK18012. You can file RNAV on a standard flight plan form by defining the route with a series of waypoints, like this: "DXR CMK18012 LGA09011 COL09013 BLM." Where rigid preferred routes are the rule, a flight plan such as this will be accepted but ignored. Your clearance will follow the local preferred departure route or city-paired departure-arrival route. In many areas, especially away from the east coast and major terminals, you'll probably be cleared as filed.

About half the airplanes in the GA fleet have loran or GPS. That means that the rest have only VOR or VOR and DME. Even without approved RNAV aboard, you can still use RNAV en route charts to plot a direct course between two points. Just establish the waypoints as described above, then fly the course between the waypoints, applying the appropriate wind correction and course corrections as you pass each waypoint. The technique, sometimes called poor man's RNAV, is described in detail in *The Proficient Pilot*, by Barry Schiff.

Wait a minute, you ask, are we proposing you use this method to navigate on an IFR flight plan, without approved RNAV? No, we wouldn't do that. But it is a real time saver when you're navigating VFR via VORs. And under IFR, there's no reason not to ask a controller for a suggested heading or vectors, while you're using poor man's RNAV for backup.

We've saved one of our favorite little books for last: the lowly, green Airport/ Facility Directory. *While it may lack some handy airport information (like the charge cards accepted by the airport restaurant), it does contain everything you really need to know as a pilot. Plus, there are things in there that you can't find anywhere else.*

Our personal preference is to keep a copy of AOPA's Aviation USA *around for information about businesses on the field, plus the current* A/FD *for the real scoop on the airport, itself. It's cheap insurance.*

Do You Really Need the A/FD?

With very little effort—and perhaps despite determined resistance—the average pilot can find himself hopelessly awash in trivial data. The government spews out mountains of aviation-related information, which publishers like us cleverly repackage and sell by the ton, clogging the mails and generally making your life far more complicated than it ought to be. (Hey, we didn't start it, we're just carrying on the tradition.)

In the midst of all this is the stodgy government *Airport/Facility Directory*, the Herman Stooldrear of the flight data world. Pilots generally know about the A/FD, but not many know exactly what it's for nor do they agree on whether it's required reading. The A/FD is usually sold by retailers who handle NOS products and we're told by some dealers that customers who purchase charts and plates often do not bother with the A/FD. The question is, are they supposed to and what are they missing by not having the A/FD in the cockpit?

The official, squeaky clean answer is that the A/FD contains supplemental information that can't be readily depicted in graphic form. As such, it's considered a critical element of the NOS charting system, which includes low-altitude charts, IAP booklets, sectionals and/or WACs and the fortnightly Notices to Airman. Although they don't say it in so many words, the government implies that pilots must have the A/FD; it's not an optional publication. Of course, the feds make the same assumption about the published notams booklet and hardly anyone subscribes to it.

Still, the question remains, if you've got a full-blown Jepps subscription and perhaps a good flight guide, like the J-Aid or *AOPA's Aviation USA*, do you really need the A/FD? It is possible to obtain through other sources quite a bit of what the A/FD contains. But "quite a bit" is not the same as "all." Maddeningly, even though commercial publishers do a better job of packaging flight guide and airport data, the government wins on thoroughness. You will find data in the A/FD that's not available elsewhere.

The official purpose of the A/FD is to provide an approved source of airport, facility and navaid data and to act as an adjunct to the instrument and visual charts published by NOS. As are instrument charts and plates, the A/FD is issued every 56 days and is effective on the airspace cycle.

The airport entries contain all the essentials; runway lengths and alignments, lighting, elevation, navaid types and frequencies, approaches and so on. This data is duplicated in both NOS and Jeppesen approach plates, however and we know plenty of pilots of who fly regularly (and safely) without ever consulting the A/FD.

Okay, what about the gotcha's? The A/FD has some data that will help you avoid them. A couple of years ago, we were flying into an Ohio airport and happened to see this note in the A/FD: "Special Air Traffic Rules-Part 93, see Regulatory Notices." Paging to that section of the A/FD, we learned that at this particular airport, pilots are supposed to enter the pattern from the north and fly right traffic. (This is a regulation, not a recommendation.)

Jeppesen carried a sketchy explanation of this quirky pattern entry on the airport diagram. The NOS plate had nothing at all about it. Both the J-Aid and *Aviation USA* did have it. You can see that by relying on just your plates, you could get burned. The A/FD's airport section also has nice-to-know stuff related to local procedures and customs. It's bad form to have the Unicom operator spank you for making touch and goes when a plain-as-day note in the A/FD requests just the opposite. The same applies to noise abatement procedures. The A/FD often has them when the other guides don't.

One word of caution on airport entries: We've found that information on services, fuel available and the relevant phone number is often out of date or just plain wrong. If fuel and services are important, phone ahead and check it out yourself.

As its title implies, the A/FD includes data on navaids that isn't available elsewhere. This includes type, class, location and elevation of navaids, plus any restrictions that might apply. Nearly a third of all VORs are restricted in some way and the A/FD is the only way to find out about them. The J-Aid has basic data on navaids but nothing on restrictions.

In the back of the A/FD, you'll find sections on VOR checkpoints, facility phone numbers and frequencies and IFR preferred routes. Again, this is also in J-Aid (or in Jeppesen's regular coverage) but it's not found in VFR flight guides. For what it's worth, we find the A/FD's format on preferred routes more readable than Jeppesen's. But, in both cases, the preferred route data is often woefully behind what ATC is actually doing.

Since sectionals are an indispensable part of IFR flying, you need to keep them current. Again, the A/FD is the only way. Revisions and corrections to sectionals published between the six-month issuance dates are posted at the back of the A/FD. Most of these aren't critical but, occasionally, you'll find a badly needed frequency or an airport identifier change. Better to have it than not, in our view.

If you're an NOS subscriber, you really don't have much choice on the A/FD. It's part of the government system and we think you ought to get it, along with the fortnightly Notices to Airmen. If you're a Jeppesen subscriber and you're taking the J-Aid, buying the A/FD will duplicate some of what you're getting.

Jeppesen says the A/FD isn't a necessity for its subscribers, whether they take the J-Aid or not. However, even though Jeppesen's own notam service is fairly complete, it does recommend that subscribers take the published notams.

As we've said in the past, we're not sure the published notams are worth the money or the effort. Because Jeppesen revises twice monthly and provides much of what's in the published notams, you can probably get by without subscribing.

Since Part 91 drivers (and small-time 135 pilots, too) don't have company dispatch to take care of the little details, we reluctantly conclude that the A/FD is a must, even for Jeppesen subscribers. Since Jeppesen is already providing much of the notam data but not much of what's in the A/FD, having the little green booklets is cheap insurance.

• Section Two •

Behind
the
Scenes

How Approaches
are Created

Have you ever wondered how an instrument approach is developed? Most of us don't give it a
second thought. We use IFR charts with 100 per-
cent confidence that someone carefully designed the procedure and flight
checked it before approving it for printing and distribution.

To the IFR cognoscente, it's a serious misunderstanding of instrument
flying to think of an approach plate as a mere map for dropping out of the clouds
in search of a runway. At the very least, a plate is a work of art and for the true
zealot, it's a symbol of man's continuing struggle against the forces of nature.
For us hackers, a plate is just another darned revision to post.

Still, you've got to appreciate what's inside those brown envelopes Jeppesen
sends every two weeks, if for no other reason than they represent a lot of work
by some very dedicated people. Before an approach even gets to Jeppesen (or
NOS) however, someone has to dream it up, draw it and actually fly it. As you
might imagine, it's an involved process.

Works in Progress

One would think that, like the Interstate highway system, the airspace
infrastructure would be pretty much settled by now. Yet there are still
a lot of revisions to deal with, some of them major. Things change over
time: new towers and buildings are constructed, airports are altered,
and FAA is constantly fiddling with the design of the airspace to
enhance traffic flow.

Over the course of an average year, the FAA's field offices work on
hundreds of approaches; a relatively small number—no more than 10
percent—are brand new, clean-sheet procedures. Why so few new

procedures? Chiefly because the number of airports in the U.S. is declining. Many existing airports simply don't qualify for approaches, either because they don't have the necessary navaids or because obstacle or other insurmountable problems rule out an approach.

GPS (and to a lesser extent loran) may eliminate the navaid shortage but with man-made obstacles popping up like weeds, some airports never will get approaches, or at least if they do, the minimums won't be low enough to make them worth much.

Still, requests for new procedures trickle into the FAA at a regular clip, originating from any of a half dozen sources. The agency maintains an open-door policy, which is to say that anyone can ask for a new approach and have the request taken seriously. Typically, requests come from airport operators, airline, charter and corporate operators, state aviation groups and occasionally individual pilots.

Want to carve out a runway on the lower 40 and plant an NDB on your new field? The FAA will be happy to discuss an approach, even if they end up rejecting your request. (It never hurts to ask.) If they do approve it, congratulations. You get to write a big check to cover the government's costs in developing and flight checking the approach. Plan on five or six figures, at least.

A fair number of new approaches originate within the FAA itself, at the local Flight Inspection Field Offices (FIFO), often after a flight check has revealed problems with an existing procedure. Even though originated by the FAA, these new approaches go through the same approval process as those requested by airports and individual users.

Rule-making process

We take for granted that to legally fly an approach, all we need is an NOS or Jeppesen chart. To be a legal procedure, it must first be published in narrative form as proposed rule-making under FAR 97. As soon as the procedure is adopted as part of FAR 97, NOS and other agencies can publish the charts. While it's actually legal to fly an approach using just the narrative description, it would be very difficult.

Don't attempt to purchase FAR 97 from the Government Printing Office in order to get all approach procedures in narrative form. Copies of the narratives aren't filed in FAR 97, but are on file for the entire U.S. at the FAA National Flight Data Center in Washington, D.C., and by region at FAA Regional Offices and Flight Inspection Field Offices.

Like just about everything else FAA does, the approach-building process is subject to the inevitable public comment.

Before establishing or revising instrument procedures, the FAA allows comments from aviation organizations, pilots, airport manag-

Brad Rush constructs obstruction traps on the Rutland quadrangle.

ers, etc. For example, a communications company built a transmitter tower near the airport at which we base our airplane. The FAA determined that an instrument departure procedure was necessary. Before implementing the procedure, the airport manager and local pilots were given the opportunity to comment. The resulting procedure required a minimum climb gradient for instrument departures.

Checking the boxes

The FAA's flow chart for inventing a new approach makes Rube Goldberg look like a minimalist. It has 76 separate steps, plus a long list of supplementary items. Ominously, a few of the steps have nasty feedback loops that have proved the undoing of more than one proposed approach. If you're getting the idea that this isn't a simple process, you're right. When a crisp new plate arrives in the mail, it represents the tip of paperwork iceberg spanning many months (sometimes years) of document shuffling.

Most new approaches begin life at the local FAA regional office. Each region (there are nine) has a group of specialists whose job is to sift through requests for new procedures and to scrutinize revisions in those that already exist. With one exception, the actual nuts-and-bolts plotting of a new approach is done by the FIFOs but before it gets to that stage, the FAA regional office gets its say.

Region's review includes navaid availability, airport layout, obstacles, communications, weather reporting and something like a dozen other considerations. Obviously, there's little point in designing an approach if some insurmountable obstacle (literally or figuratively) will cause it to fail flight check. The region will also decide on "community needs," which is a polite way of saying they'll definitely decline your request for a Cat I ILS to a turf strip serving six airplanes, unless of course you're springing for the equipment.

Off to FIFO

If region's review turns up no horrors, the approach-to-be becomes a contender and off it goes to FIFO in the form of a fat file containing all the preliminary data. FIFOs are the guys who buzz around in King Airs flight checking approaches. In addition to being pilots, the FIFO staffers are trained in ways of TERPS; when they're not flying flight check, they're back at the office crunching data or they're hunched over the drawing board and computer terminal deeply enmeshed in the rather

Computerized plots help, but designing an approach still requires a lot of tedious drawing on quadrangle charts.

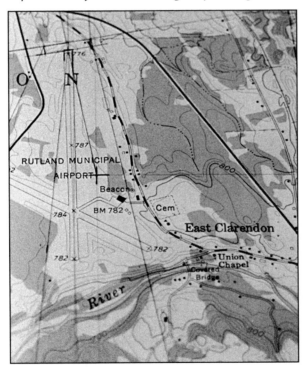

tedious job of designing and checking approaches.

The exception to FIFO's grinding out the procedures, by the way, is a relatively new working group in Oklahoma City devoted exclusively to developing new procedures. In a sense, this group—called AVN-270—is the SWAT team of the approach world, in that it works independently of the usual FIFO loop. AVN-270 was organized in 1989 specifically to build MLS approaches and the hundreds of loran procedures that were supposed to open the outback to IFR operations.

AVN-270 has done its part; dozens of loran procedures have been completed and every one of them rests peacefully unpublished in its own file, awaiting the day when loran is approved for approaches—which, with the advent of GPS, seems unlikely. Meanwhile, AVN-270's specialists—mostly former military approach designers who aren't necessarily pilots—have been assigned more pressing work.

When we visited them, the group's 16 specialists were working on approaches for Denver's new airport and, because of short staffing, they were also helping with overflow work from some of the FIFOs, including procedures for New England normally handled by the Atlantic City FIFO. We spent the day with Brad Rush, a former Air Force specialist assigned to cover New England. He was busy developing a new loran approach to runway 1 at Rutland, Vermont.

In some ways, a loran approach is atypical of how approaches have been designed historically. Because they're based on wide area navigation rather than fixed local navaids, loran procedures aren't as limiting as an off-airport VOR or NDB. Fixes and courses can be moved around more or less at will to align with runways or dodge obstacles. Still, the designer has to step through the same hoops no matter what the navaid and if GPS really does come into its own for approaches on a national basis, the growing bank of loran procedures may serve as templates. We expect many loran approaches will simply be tweaked up and relabeled as "RNAV/LORAN/GPS" procedures.

Intro to TERPS

Some plates are so cluttered with extraneous detail that we tend to forget that the sole purpose of an approach is to allow an orderly descent to the airport without hitting anything. Safely achieving this goal drives the approach design process, from beginning to end.

As is the case in everything the government gets it mitts on, there's a standard in the form a esoteric manual known as TERPS. This stands for "U.S. Standard for Terminal Instrument Procedures." Where one gets an acronym like TERPS from that is beyond us. Suffice to say that TERPS is a dry-as-dust tome divided into sections corresponding to the five approach segments—transition, initial, intermediate, final and missed—plus a separate chapter for each class of approach; ILS, LOC, VOR, NDB and so on.

When a proposed approach arrives from region, a FIFO specialist (or in this case, AVN-270) reviews it in some detail, with TERPS cautions and requirements in mind. If the approach is to a newly designated IFR airport, someone from the FIFO will go visit, notebook in hand. Charts, phone interviews and aerial photographs are informative, but they're no substitute for flying into a new airport and eyeballing the country-side. It only takes one uncharted obstacle or an erroneous survey entry to unseat the entire process.

The TERPS manual requires the following guidelines when designing approach procedures:
• Standards are based on reasonable assessment of the factors that contribute to errors in aircraft navigation and maneuvering. They are designed primarily to assure that safe flight operations for all users result from their application.
• The dimensions of the obstacle clearance areas are influenced by the need to provide for a smooth, simply computed progression to and from the en route system.
• Every effort is made to formulate procedures in accordance with TERPS standards; however, peculiarities of terrain, navigation information, obstacles or traffic congestion may require special consideration when justified by operational requirements.

TERPS Obstacle Clearance Standards

Approach Segment	Primary Area	Secondary Area
Initial	1000 ft	500 ft
Intermediate	500 ft	500 ft
Final		
VOR/DME, VOR w/FAF, straight-in	250 ft	250 ft
VOR/DME, radial or arc final	500 ft	500 ft
NDB on airport, no FAF, straight-in	350 ft	350 ft
NDB w/FAF, straight-in	300 ft	300 ft
Localizer, LDA, SDF	250 ft	250 ft
Circling	300 ft	0 ft
Holding (level)	1000 ft	500 ft

• Non-standard procedures can be approved if they are fully documented and an equivalent level of safety exists. These must be studied first to insure that safety isn't degraded. For example, sometimes a military procedure deviates from FAA standards due to operational requirements. When this occurs and an equivalent level of safety is not achieved, the approach chart is marked, NOT FOR CIVIL USE.

According to TERPS requirements, an approach procedure can have five separate segments: initial, intermediate, final, circling and missed approach segments. Each segment has its own design criteria.

1. Initial approach segment—This segment begins at the initial approach fix and is where you depart the en route phase and maneuver to the intermediate segment. If an intermediate fix is part of the en route structure, an initial approach segment might not be necessary. The initial approach segment can be a DME arc, radial, course, heading, radar vector or any combination of these.

2. Intermediate approach segment—This segment transitions you from the initial approach segment to the final approach segment. This is normally where you should make aircraft configuration, speed and position adjustments before the final approach segment. The intermediate segment begins at the intermediate fix or point, requires positive course guidance, and ends at the final approach fix.

3. Final approach segment—This segment is where alignment and descent for landing is accomplished and begins at the FAF or point (some approaches don't have an FAF) and ends at the runway or missed approach point.

4. Circling approach area—This obstacle clearance area is provided for aircraft maneuvering to land on a runway that isn't aligned with the final approach course. The circling area may be established to accommodate up to five categories (A through E) of aircraft. The circling area radii are based on 1.3 Vso for the maximum certificated landing weight. When obstacles or terrain interfere, circling approaches aren't allowed or are limited to those aircraft categories that can be protected in the circling area.

5. Missed approach segment—Every approach must have a missed approach procedure that specifies an altitude and, if possible, a clearance limit. Whenever possible, the missed approach course is a continuation of the final segment.

Each approach segment consists of a primary and secondary area for obstacle clearance, except for the circling approach area, which has only a primary obstacle clearance area. On an initial approach segment, for

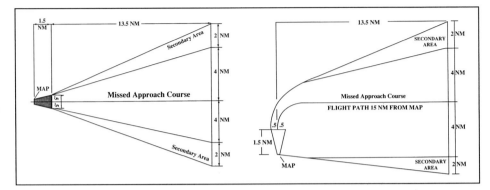

Primary and secondary obstacle clearance areas for straight-out and turning missed approaches. The secondary area tapers to zero at the outer edge. Although a generous primary obstacle clearance area is provided, you have no way of knowing if you've strayed outside of it. This is a good reason to stay as close to the centerline as possible.

example, 1000 feet of clearance is provided in the primary area, but in the secondary area, 500 feet is provided at the inner edge, but this tapers to zero feet at the outer edge.

There is some margin for error; however, poor pilot technique coupled with strong winds and turbulence can compromise safety if you don't stay on the centerline.

Obstacle clearance on the final approach segment varies for each type of non-precision approach. During an ILS, obstacle clearance is dependent on your staying on the glideslope.

The cruel world

In an approach designer's dream world, there's an unrestricted navaid on every airport and no obstacles higher than 10 feet within 100 miles of the runway. Ideally, the navaid would be on casters so it could be moved freely about the airport. Too bad the real world is never so kind. GPS and loran aside, navaids are surprisingly sparse. Even airports in the pan-flat Great Plains have obstacles to contend with and as cellular and microwave towers proliferate, things seem to get worse by the day.

At Rutland, for which Rush was designing the loran approach, the airport is literally surrounded by high terrain and obstacles, some within 3 miles of the airport. You can get a sense of an airport's obstacle environment by simply reviewing the minimums for existing approaches. Rutland's existing LDA 19 has an MDA of 1680 feet (893 feet HAT) and 3 miles vis, with a 2.8 mile fly visual segment to the runway.

By comparison, LDAs in flat country are sometimes good for 300 and a mile, under ideal circumstances. Rutland's new loran approach was to come in from the south but if anything, the obstacles are worse in that direction so Rush knew the minimums wouldn't improve much, if at all.

Approach designers have several sources for locating obstacles, including airport-specific Obstacle Charts from NOS, local quadrangle charts, ADAM (airport datum monument) surveys, satellite photos, questionnaires sent to airport operators and—for MSA circles—sectionals. Even if all the obstructions are charted—which is by no means certain—it takes a sharp eye to spot everything.

A certain level of automation is available from a system called IAPA or Instrument Approach Procedures Automation. Essentially, IAPA is an obstacle and airport database that's capable of plotting approach courses with TERPS criteria in mind. By modern CAD-CAM standards, IAPA's capabilities are pretty rudimentary. It's relatively slow and its database is entirely lacking information on natural, terrain obstacles. The FAA is developing an improved version of this system called—surprise, Advanced IAPA. It's supposed to be on line in 1994 or 1995.

Beginning at the end

The lowest possible minimums are what any new approach is all about. TERPS' ideal world allows for pretty impressive minimums on a loran procedure: a 250-foot HAT with 1/2-mile visibility on a runway that's equipped with approach lights. Of course, because of obstacles, it goes up from there and in the case of Rutland, way up.

Considering that hills, trees and towers litter the landscape, Rush explained that if anything is going to eventually kill a new procedure, it's better to find out about it sooner than later. For that reason, most approach designers work from the inside out, by designing the final and missed approach segments first.

"If you can't get them to work out, you're dead in the water right from the start," he explained.

At airports like Rutland, the challenge is to thread the final approach course through the obstacles to provide horizontal clearance or, when that won't work, to devise stepdown altitudes for vertical clearance. This is accomplished by constructing what's called an obstacle clearance trapezoid and placing it over the airport along what appear to be plausible courses. In the good old days, the trap was drawn by hand but now the IAPA computer does some of the grunt work. By punching in the necessary coordinates, Rush could have the computer sketch in the trapezoid, with any known man-made obstacles highlighted.

In addition to an obstacle database, the Instrument Approach Procedure Automation system (IAPA) also performs the basic connect-the-dots tasks of approach design.

Every type of approach has a trapezoid of a standard, specific size. For loran procedures, the trapezoid is 4 miles wide at the final approach fix and 1.2 miles wide at the runway. Its length can be anywhere from 5 to 10 miles. The area within the trapezoid is said to be the primary obstacle clearance area, meaning that the minimum vertical clearance outside the FAF is 500 feet, decreasing to 250 feet inside the FAF. A secondary clearance area outside the primary trapezoid guarantees 250 to 500 feet of clearance at its innermost edge, tapering to zero clearance at the outermost edge.

Threading the thicket

In the imaginary world of flat planes, you could simply plop the trapezoid onto the map so that the proposed course aligned with the runway, mark the FAF and missed approach point, sketch in the missed approach trapezoid (yes, it has its own) and you'd be done. But, as Rush explained, Rutland is the real world. When he aligned the course with runway 1 (proposed inbound course 013 degrees), several towers punched up through the bottom of trapezoid, not to mention trees, hills, rocks and other airplane-eating clutter.

An obvious solution is to simply raise the trapezoid so the course is 250 or 500 feet above the highest or "controlling" obstacle or to "step over" the offending object with stepdown fixes. No doubt, you've seen this done on some procedures. The specialist also has some latitude to elongate the trapezoid by moving the final approach fix further from the runway. If an obstacle just nicks the corner of the primary area, stretching the trap may help.

Sometimes these tricks work, sometimes not. It depends on where the obstacles are in relation to the airport and the final approach fix, the point at which the final descent to the runway commences.

Why not just step over the obstacle and take a screaming dive down to the MDA? Well, you might not mind that but TERPS, with its provision for every purpose, says thou shalt not. The maximum allowable descent gradient is 400 feet per mile, or 667 feet per minute at 100 knots. That doesn't mean you can't descend faster, it just means that the FAA isn't supposed to design an approach requiring a higher descent rate. Besides, as a point of pride, most designers will use the maximum descent gradients only as a last resort.

"I don't like to get in too close to the runway with a stepdown," Rush explained. "It gives you the feeling that you're nosediving at the runway, especially when you're coming out of the weather."

Considering the descent gradient and obstacles, Rush discovered that a best-case straight-in approach to Rutland's runway 1 would have minimums with an HAT of perhaps 500 to 600 feet. Not bad, considering that Rutland is the kind of a place that probably shouldn't have an airport at all, let alone one with approaches. Unfortunately, as Rush knew without even looking, those nice low HATs would never survive the rest of the design process.

The TERP turns

TERPS is so full of little turns and twists that some specialists describe it as one big gotcha. TERPS version of the law of gravity is probably its most vexing feature. Rather than insisting that what goes up must come down, TERPS decrees that what goes in, must come out and getting in is a lot easier that getting out. In other words, planning the missed approach can be far more difficult than threading the needle into the airport, especially around mountains.

There are two reasons for this. One is that the missed approach trap is much larger; 15 miles long and 12 miles wide, at the widest end. This accounts for the fact that pilots don't really expect to miss and that there's likely to be a certain amount of wandering around until the airplane gets established on the missed approach course.

Second, because you can usually descend a lot faster than you can climb, the FAA insists that the missed approach segment be obstacle-

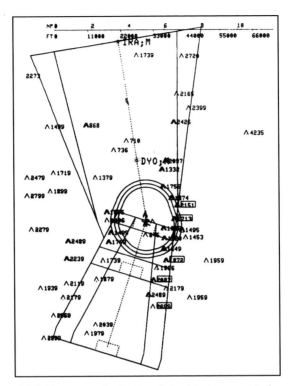

IAPA's output for Rutland depicts trapezoids for the final approach and missed approach segments. The primary obstacle protection areas are represented by the outer bands of the trapezoids.

free for a climb gradient of only 152 feet per mile or a measly 250 feet per minute at 100 knots. This is the chief reason that Rutland's LDA requires 3 miles of vis. To safely clear the terrain south of the airport in the event of a missed, the LDA's MAP had to be moved back a couple of miles and that required the designer to specify the 2.8 mile fly-visual segment.

When Rush punched data for the missed segment into the IAPA, even I could see he had a big problem. Hills north of the airport bristle with towers and trees and these punched up through the bottom of the missed approach trap like a pin cushion. He tried reorienting the trap to the west but its primary area was simply too large to avoid all of the obstacles. Obviously, the only way to meet the missed approach climb gradient was keep airplanes from descending too deeply into the bowl on the inbound and that meant—right—higher minimums.

You'd think it would be an easy matter to jack up the MDA and leave it at that, but it doesn't work that way. If Rush had done that here, he would have had an MDA up around 3000 feet and the new approach would be even less useful than the existing LDA. Instead, he used TERPS' myriad conditions and provisions to nibble away at the problem, inching the minimums up in increments of 50 or 60 feet until the missed approach criteria were satisfied.

Give and take

One early compromise was straight-in minimums. By shifting the course well to the west (32 degrees for the inbound), the missed approach course turned more sharply to the left, veering away from the obstacles northeast of the airport. That course alignment also moved the final approach trap away from some troublesome obstacles due south of the airport. This meant that the loran approach would have circling-only minimums but in exchange for that compromise, Rush was able to propose a somewhat lower MDA.

To gain some more clearance for the inbound course, Rush moved the FAF back from the minimum of 5 miles to 7 miles. This stretched and narrowed the trapezoid and moved the controlling obstacles from the primary into the secondary area. With a longer, narrower trap, Rush was able to position a stepdown fix 2-1/2 miles from the runway; this provided clearance over the close-in obstacles and produced a descent gradient of 392 feet per mile. That's not ideal by any means but it's flyable, at least. Besides, at an airport like Rutland, you're lucky to have it that good.

All of these machinations would have produced circling-only minimums of 1168 feet HAA (practically identical to the LDA) were it not for the fact that TERPS never gives up anything without a price. In this case, Rush's penalties added up this way: Add 50 feet for excessive length of final (6 miles is the cutoff, he stretched the trap to 7 miles); add 60 feet for the missed approach gradient; add 80 feet to meet the descent gradient between the FAF and the stepdown.

The proverbial bottom line? An MDA of 2100 feet for a height above airport of 1313 feet, with visibility of 1-1/4 mile for Cat As, 1-1/2 mile for Bs and 3 miles for Cs. Cat Ds can go elsewhere, thanks. Overall, it's not a bad approach but in really low weather—which Rutland does get in ski season—we'd be inclined to shoot the ILS at Glens Falls and rent a car. It just doesn't make a lot of sense to fly into mountainous airports without an ILS.

The end game

Having satisfied himself that the approach and minimums were workable, Rush drew the traps onto the Rutland quadrangle chart and checked yet again for any obstacles he may have missed. The rest is just filling out forms to convey the new approach to a FIFO for flight check. Normally, the Atlantic city FIFO would check Rutland but the OKC office will be flying all of the loran approaches.

We don't expect it to happen anytime soon. When and if the procedure is flight checked and given the FIFO's blessing, it'll be sent off to the National Flight Data Center, officially logged into federal records and eventually sent off to Jeppesen (and NOS) for charting, whence it arrives in your mailbox begging to be posted. As should be obvious by now, compared to what Rush and his colleagues have to do, you've got it easy.

Double-Checking
the Approach

I n the last chapter we saw how FAA goes about devising a new approach. But that's only part of the equation: it's also necessary to actually try it out to see if it works, then periodically check up on it to make sure that it's still working the way it did when it was commissioned.

We went along for a ride in one of FAA's custom-built King Air 300s to see how the process works.

A Day With Flight Check

A couple of years ago, over lunch, we were explaining the magic of the ILS to a group business associates who had just flown in commercial and landed at Kennedy in Cat II weather. On a napkin, we sketched out the localizer and glideslope, drew in the markers, the whole bit. We were certain they'd be awestruck at the wonders of all-weather navigation and would never again take for granted the airlines' ability to land on a fog-bound runway.

They thought we were making up the whole thing.

"This seems insane to me," said one of our colleagues. "You mean you follow this little beam all the way to the ground without seeing anything?"

"Well, yes, but it's not really a beam, it's a..."

"How do you know the beam is where it's supposed to be?"

"Ah...well, they check it out every so often and you'd know if it wasn't right."

We thought of that conversation a few years later when we dusted off the same glib explanation to answer a sharp student's question about ILS accuracy. His obvious rejoinder—who checks it and how often?—exhausted our knowledge of the topic. By then, we'd been chased away from the localizer by an FAA Flight Check aircraft so we knew somebody was checking *something*, but just what these guys do was as mysterious to us as the ILS was baffling to our friends. So a few years ago, we got ourselves invited along on a Flight Check mission out of Atlantic City, N.J.

Besides being the home of FAA's Technical Center (a skunkworks for new navaids, radar, computers and so on) ACY has a Flight Inspection Field Office. It's one of five in the U.S. whose job is to inspect every single public navigation and approach aid and, by request, the private ones too.

ACY's custom-built King Airs cover New England and the mid-Atlantic states, as far south as Virginia plus a few military aids in Canada. Most of the facilities—there are about 2,000—get an airborne check at least once a year, some more often. If that sounds like a lot of flying, it is: Atlantic City's aircraft log between 3,000 and 4,000 hours a year.

Most of it's routine flying. Modern navaids are reliable enough to justify a pilot's blind faith in flying an ILS to minimums but they aren't bulletproof. Some of the equipment is showing its age. Circuits drift out of tolerance; cables and connectors corrode; antennas become misaligned. Sometimes they just quit for no apparent reason. It's Flight Check's job to diagnose problems and see that they're fixed.

A late start

Our tour with Flight Check was somewhat atypical in that it was a day mission with an evening return to ACY. The King Airs usually embark upon week-long treks, collecting data on navaids in a given area, then returning it to base for analysis. We also surveyed an unusual variety of navaids that included ILSs, PARs, an NDB and a proposed new airway. Before our departure, the aircraft commander, Newell McCalmont, spent a half hour on the phone, coordinating the day's work with the ATC and maintenance people we would be talking to along the way. Our route would take us on a loop through Virginia, West Virginia, Pennsylvania and finally back to New Jersey.

Our aircraft was N82, a year-old BE-300 in the FAA's government-issue blue and white livery. Although it operates a few other types, the 300—or at least the FAA's version of it—has become the standard flight check aircraft, having replaced a fleet of aging, fuel-guzzling Sabreliners. Although they look like off-the-shelf models, Flight Check's King Airs are custom manufactured for the FAA under a unique type certificate. They have an extra air conditioner to keep the aircraft's considerable avionics from frying and an APU so nav equipment can be initialized on the ground.

A maintenance squawk delayed our departure for an hour or so but once it was sorted out, we launched into crisp VMC, southbound to Norfolk, Va. for a look at a pair of ILSs. Flight check crews will work in IMC but they prefer not to. It slows the work and makes it impossible to see new obstacles and verify ground checkpoints that are helpful in surveying approaches and airways.

Enroute, while we fumbled with an intercom panel with no less than eight separate knobs, technician Clive Gale explained the onboard gizmos. All but one of the seats on the left side of the aircraft have been removed to make room for an electronics bay housing the navigation computer unit, which is itself part of a larger system called the AFIS, for Automatic Flight Inspection System.

In simple terms, what the AFIS does (among other things) is to compare the actual position of a navigation signal—say a localizer or a radial—with where it's really supposed to be. It does this by tying together a laser-ring gyro inertial navigation system that's initialized on the ramp at departure with a multi-DME RNAV system. The aircraft's position is continually updated, both by reinitialization of the INS over known positions (runway thresholds) and by an allied system that fixes position with range data from the six closest DMEs or TACANs.

A purpose-made, onboard computer merges information from each source and continuously calculates present position accurate to within a few hundred feet. The computer contains a data base with technical specs—frequencies, distances, elevations, courses, local variation, and the like—on all the navaids in the aircraft's area of operation. It knows, for example, the frequencies of all the DMEs and TACANs and automatically tunes and locks into the six best ones for calculating a fix.

As the airplane is flown through the prescribed procedure, the AFIS crunches its data, then displays the results on a screen for evaluation. A three-foot-long printout, looking rather like an oversized EKG, records the data for review later. While a check is in progress—or even just droning down the airway from one site to another—the AFIS' nav data can be coupled with the airplane's autopilot, creating an astonishingly accurate INS-RNAV.

Down the barrel

The day's first job was to check a pair of ILSs at Norfolk. Where practical, Flight Checks are supposed to be accommodated with no delay. ATC is given notice of an impending check but the word doesn't always filter down to the radar room. Controllers have to be resourceful when a Flight Check aircraft is in their airspace, for more than likely it will want to fly down the active runway in the *opposite* direction. While Norfolk adjusted its departures and got the inactive ILS on the air, we did 360s over Cape Charles.

FIFOs do a half-dozen different types of inspection, including commissioning, periodic, special and after-accident. Today's checks were to be periodic checks of Category I ILSs. These are done once a year.

Typically, an ILS check is done in three maneuvers, one to sense the signal strength and shape, another to measure the glideslope angle and a third to check the localizer alignment. Because we were flying a periodic check, only one of each was required. However, more extensive checks, say a Cat II ILS, may require as many ten repetitions for each approach.

The first maneuver is a ten-mile arc, flown across the localizer centerline. Tuned into the localizer frequency, the AFIS checks for "clearance," a technical term describing the signal's width, symmetry and strength. It also looks for the presence of false signals.

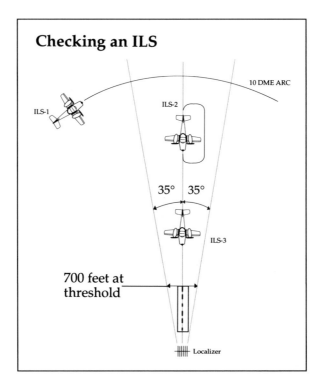

Checking an ILS

ILS-1

ILS-2

10 DME ARC

35° 35°

ILS-3

700 feet at
threshold

Localizer

The second maneuver, a turn around the hold (usually over the outer marker) feeds the AFIS computer data to calculate the glideslope angle. This is done by comparing the glideslope centerline over a known point to "tape line altitude," literally the altitude as though measured straight down with a tape measure. The altitude is calculated by a combination of inertial and barometric data.

The last check is a coupled ILS, right "down the barrel" through DH and along the length of the runway at 50 ft. to check both the localizer and the glideslope. The low pass makes it easier for the pilots to visually check localizer alignment. They're happy if its alignment at the threshold is within the width of the runway centerline, or about three feet. At both ends of the runway, during the low pass, the copilot pushes a button that, in effect, tells the AFIS computer "you're exactly here." After considering the new position data for a couple of minutes, the AFIS issues its verdict: the ILS either passes or it flunks. Minor tweaks are often done by a ground technician, on the spot while the aircraft orbits, ready to fly another check.

Flight inspectors have the authority to immediately shut down an out-of-tolerance facility. But theoretically, a really brain-dead ILS or VOR shouldn't even be on the air. Navaids are equipped with monitors that automatically shut them down if they exceed safe tolerances. Nonetheless, Flight Check crews encounter their share of weird stuff. During unusually dry weather, soil is less reflective, which can measurably distort the glideslope angle. Pilots might not notice it at the marker, but the approach won't pass inspection. Airport construction is a recurring problem. At Philadelphia International, interference from a new hangar rendered one of the airport's ILSs unusable. The company that built the hangar paid to have the system relocated.

You fly NDBs?

After we checked Norfolk's ILSs (they passed), McCalmont took radar vectors for a short hop over to Oceana Naval Air Station, where we spent the rest of the morning dodging F-14s and A-6s while we checked the base's PARs. In a rare example of interagency cooperation, the military relies on the FAA to flight check its approaches at both domestic and foreign bases. By day's end, half the crew's flight time was devoted to military work, first at Oceana, then at Lakehurst and McGuire Air Force Base in New Jersey.

Compared to the ILS, flight checking a PAR is surprisingly seat-of-the-pants. A PAR doesn't transmit a signal that the aircraft can receive so the King Air's equipment doesn't really have much to analyze. While McCalmont hand-flew the approaches, tracking the glidepath accord-

Where Intersections Come From

An *IFR* quiz on enroute charts prompted a number of reader questions on how airway intersections are determined. During our tour of the Atlantic City FIFO, we got the short course on how it's done.

The primary criteria for an airway intersection or fix is traffic flow. A request for a new fix or the moving of an existing one can come from a variety of sources but most begin with ATC; a tower or a radar facility. Ideally, an intersection should be definable by convenient navaids but, as flight check pilots sometimes discover, that doesn't always work. For survey purposes, an intersection is plotted in lat-long coordinates, accurate to .01 nautical second. That's a point about a foot square if you're picking nits.

When an intersection is proposed, the radials (or bearings) that will define it are also identified. It's up to Flight Check to determine if the selected radials will actually fix the intersection. The Flight Check aircraft first flies the centerline of the radials defining the intersection. To test the width of the proposed airway, two passes are made four miles to either side of the intersection or, when the intersection is more than 50.8 miles from the VOR, 4 1/2 degrees to either side of the intersection.

If the radials actually do define the fix, the intersection is officially approved. It gets a name and is added to the next chart revision. The National Flight Data Center names the fixes according to simple rules: the name has to have five letters, be pronounceable and have no lewd meaning. The radials that define the intersection—that is, the ones that Flight Check actually surveyed—are depicted on the chart by an arrow pointing toward the intersection. If DME is authorized to identify the intersection, the arrowhead is open. If not, it's a solid blue arrowhead. A radial without an arrow— whether an airway or not—wasn't proven by Flight Check and isn't guaranteed to define the fix. Use an unsurveyed radial at your own risk.

It's not unusual to have a proposed intersection flunk the survey. "I once climbed to flight level 230 trying to receive the right radial. I finally gave up," said L.C. Loman, one of ACY's inspection pilots. In that case, another radial is selected or the intersection is moved where pilots can find it.

ing to the controller's calls and eyeballing the course alignment, Gale manually updated the computer then calculated the glidepath angles for each approach. All were slightly low. One was well to the left of course, a fact that was obvious even from our vantage point in the rear of the aircraft. The crew offered to orbit while technicians adjusted the radar but the controllers declined. We stowed the gear and got an IFR pop-up to Dulles International, where we stopped for lunch and 450 gallons of Jet-A.

After lunch, co-pilot Curt Draper moved into the King Air's left seat and we headed for the next job, an NDB to Upperville, Va., a private airport 18 miles west of Dulles. With 5,100 feet of asphalt runway, Upperville is hardly the farmer's pea patch most of us think of as a private strip. As do many private fields, however, Upperville has an unpublished approach. Any airport owner who's willing to pay for it can have an approach designed by the government, including an ILS, if the field warrants it. There's no requirement to do so, but for a fee, the FAA will flight check the approach. Our little fly-by probably cost the owner a couple of grand—chump change for anybody who can afford to build a mile of hard runway in the Virginia countryside.

Before we left Atlantic City, we'd told the crew that we fly a lot of NDBs, for training and occasionally in actual IMC. McCalmont smiled and half-jokingly blessed me with the sign-of-the-cross. After we had surveyed Upperville, we could see why. Compared to the ILS, there's really not much to checking an NDB. So long as the ADF needle doesn't swing any more than five degrees either side of course and there are no obvious obstacles, the approach is up to spec.

Airway patchwork

From Upperville, we set about another of Flight Check's major tasks: airway survey. VORs are periodically checked for service volume, signal quality and flyability or needle action, what the inspectors call "structure." The surveys also assure that the airways are really where the chart says they are. New VORs—there aren't many these days—get an extensive commissioning check. A great deal of routine VOR work is done automatically by an Oklahoma City-based Convair 580 that drones across the country at FL230 along precise grid lines. Any anomalies it finds are flagged for detailed inspection by the regional FIDOs.

On our flight, the crew had been been asked to prove a new airway southwest of the Harrisburg VOR. For months, the VOR, defying repair, had transmitted an unusable signal. Attempting to cobble around it, ATC had proposed a new airway with a 3,000 foot MEA, based on a radial from the Selinsgrove VOR, just north of Harrisburg.

Harrisburg: The VOR From Hell

The VOR we visited on our trip with Flight Check—Harrisburg, Pennsylvania—is notorious among pilots in the area for being virtually useless as a navaid.

The FAA figures an average VOR requires about a half-year worth of man hours to maintain or about $25,000 in labor. The Harrisburg VOR has probably sucked up that much in a bad month and chances are, it'll never be fixed. Harrisburg has turned out to be a case study in how *not* to site a VOR.

It was originally sited five miles west of the city of Harrisburg, on rolling terrain that's typical of central Pennsylvania. The VOR's radiation pattern was never satisfactory, however, so in 1987, it was moved several miles north, onto land managed by the state game commission. Besides improving the signal, moving the VOR also played prominently in the FAA's expanded east coast plan, a major restructure of airways and preferred routes.

Unfortunately, the new site proved little better (and perhaps worse) than the original. The VOR was such a mess in early 1990, that all of the airways it defined were notam'd NA and so marked on the low-altitude charts, a relatively rare occurrence. The situation didn't improve much despite a great deal of work: two years later, 47 radials were still completely unusable and most of the others were restricted at various altitudes and distances.

No one seems to know exactly why this VOR has been so troublesome but its location atop an undulating ridge is thought to be the main contributing cause, with nearby trees aiding and abetting. You'd think a hilltop location would be ideal but this particular hill is cut through with notches and valleys which bounce the signal around like a rubber check in a tile bathroom. Like your local theater troupe, the VOR has a performing season. During the winter, when the trees are bare and lacking sap flow, it works better than in the summer, when leaves attenuate the signal.

The FAA has spent thousands in site work and flight checks. They've tried modifying the counterpoise, trimming the trees, even changing the frequency. Some radials have been brought back but the VOR is still one of the most restricted navaids in the country. Conversion to Doppler (mid-1990s) will help but ultimately, true salvation awaits the day when the VOR can be trucked off the mountain to the boneyard, rendered obsolete by GPS.

They had hoped for a usable signal 70 miles from the VOR. That's a reach in flat country and it's not flat around Harrisburg. After punching the setup into his keyboard, Gale rolled his eyes: "This one's a prayer."

Sometimes, if everything's just right, a VOR is usable far beyond its standard service volume. Not today. Fifty miles out, the signal was strong enough to knock the flags off but not good enough for an airway. Normally, the aircraft would climb in 1,000 foot increments until a reliable signal is received, thereby establishing MEA and plotting changeover points. But the crew had a 4 p.m. appointment to check the ILS at McGuire Air Force Base so the task was left for another day.

Back to base

On the way back to ACY, we checked a couple of TACANs at Lakehurst Naval Air Station then landed for a fruitless search of the ground check points. The file showed they'd last been seen in 1971. The Navy forgot to repaint the checkpoints; they had simply weathered away.

By the time we arrived back on ramp at ACY, the King Air had covered some 500 miles and flown a dozen approaches. Gale carted his printouts into the office where they would be reviewed for anything the airborne analysis may have missed. Meanwhile, N82 was fueled and towed into hangar, to be made ready for the next day's work.

GPS Approaches: The Coming Thing

W hen the VOR (and the associated ILS) system was introduced decades ago, it marked a revolution in the way IFR navigation was accomplished. It still works quite well, and is likely to remain the backbone of the airspace infrastructure for years to come; but with its many quirks and its network of maintenance-intensive ground stations, most agree that it's time to retire it.

There have been a couple of different systems proposed as replacements: first there was the idea of MLS (Microwave Landing System) which promised what was, in effect, a better ILS that would allow for handy tools like curved precision approaches. Given the high capital cost (new ground stations, new— and redundant—receivers in every airplane), it never really got anywhere.

Then, with the advent of cheap airborne loran receivers and the upgrading of the system to close the mid-continent gap, it looked like loran would be the wave of the future.

Now, however, there's a new system that looks like it might really be the (eventual) replacement for the VOR: the Global Positioning System, or GPS.

As this book goes to press, the GPS satellite constellation is still not complete, and questions remain about reliability sufficient to accomodate approaches.

Still, GPS shows great promise and should prove to be the centerpiece of air navigation in the not-too-distant future.

Satellite Advances

1993 saw several major advances in the GPS arena. As the year closed, we were much closer to seeing the reality of regular GPS use for IFR than we had been the year before. Consider the events:

• The FAA approved a new Technical Standards Order (TSO) for the manufacture of IFR-certified GPS receivers.

• Manufacturers began shipping receivers that can be upgraded to meet the new TSO once the certification process is complete. One maker (Trimble) had received TSO approval by late in the year.

• The agency embarked upon an accelerated program to allow existing VOR approaches to be flown as GPS procedures.

• The Defense Department approved the GPS system for civil use in late 1993.

• The first regular non-precision GPS approaches went into use at two Colorado airports.

• Research continues on precision approaches using GPS; it may be technically feasible to construct both Cat II and Cat III ILSs based on GPS.

The big news: A new TSO

In 1993, the FAA completed work on a TSO written specifically for IFR-certifiable GPS receivers. TSO C129 covers receivers suitable for en route, terminal and approach mode, for supplemental navigation. Those who've been in the avionics game long enough to remember the FAA's foot dragging on loran admit to a certain astonishment at how quickly the agency approved the GPS TSO. In a matter of mere months, the TSO was drafted, circulated among manufacturers for revisions and approved in final form.

The GPS manufacturers we've talked to describe the TSO as a reasonable framework for the first generation of IFR GPS receivers. Research on the new spec bore its first fruit late in the year, with the certification of the Trimble TNL2000.

The new TSO gives technical specs for two broad categories and six separate classes of GPS receivers. The two major categories are boxes that have both a GPS sensor and a navigation display and those that feed data from a GPS sensor into an integrated system, such as inertial, Omega or DME-DME. The latter are more the province of heavies and high-end biz jets. Flib drivers will want the combined sensor and display sets. These are essentially identical to current loran and GPS receivers, except for having additional GPS display requirements.

The TSO allows for two classes of receivers in this category, one capable of en route and terminal navigation and one that adds non-precision approaches to those features (the aforementioned Trimble is an en route and terminal unit, not an approach aid). This is good news for avionics buyers since, presumably, a set not approved for approaches will be cheaper, thus offering some price stratification in what promises to be initially expensive equipment.

The TSO describes detailed operating characteristics GPS receivers are supposed to have. In general, it requires them to be designed to minimize pilot workload. We suspect that this requirement will eventually result in fewer control knobs and keys and databases that contain airway intersections (if not the airways themselves), airport, navaids, SIDs, STARs and all of the waypoints which will define the non-precision GPS approaches the FAA plans to publish.

Approach-approved boxes will have the approaches stored by name and when called up by the pilot, the waypoints will be automatically loaded; no manual waypoint loading will be required. As the aircraft approaches the destination airport, the receiver is supposed to display an approach-mode alert and once the pilot engages it, the receiver will automatically sequence from one approach waypoint to the next.

If you spring for one of these receivers, you'll also have to subscribe to a database update service, most likely from Jeppesen. We haven't heard any prices on database subscriptions but if they follow Jeppesen's usual two-week cycle, care and feeding of an IFR GPS receiver won't be cheap. Receivers will have either a datacard that the pilot inserts into the front of the receiver or a computer interface of some sort. So far, it doesn't look like datacards will promise relief from the biweekly misery of inserting revisions. You'll still have to buy the paper and post it in your Airway Manuals.

When's it gonna be done?

Overshadowing the growing euphoria over GPS is one sobering fact: GPS has been and will remain a toy in the military sandbox, at least for the short term. Until the system is declared operational, the FAA won't allow IFR operations with stand-alone GPS receivers, TSO'd or not. The Department of Defense's official party line is that the system is still under construction and navigation services are subject to change and interruption without notice. DOD has steadfastly refused to commit to a completion date although mid- to late 1994 seems to be a good bet.

Under enormous pressure from civil users, the Department of Defense declared that the GPS satellite network had achieved Initial Operational Capability (IOC) late in 1993, after the 21st satellite had been launched. Most of these are Block II vehicles, which are those which will ultimately comprise the full-up constellation. The remainder are Block I development satellites.

Originally, the Air Force said the GPS constellation would be declared operational when 24 Block IIs were on orbit. (Three of those satellites are considered spares.)

Unless other technical glitches surface, the FAA says it's willing to allow supplemental GPS navigation under IOC. Full Operational Capability—FOC, of course—is now the military's definition of GPS completion. It may not occur until 1994 or 1995.

In the latest development, in September1993 FAA approved the first two GPS approaches. Special authorization was granted to Continental Express Airlines to make use of non-precision GPS approaches at Aspen and Steamboat Springs, Colorado. These approaches were being flown using now-obsolete early generation MLS procedures.

Integrity problems

Even with 24 satellites on orbit, signal integrity remains an issue and until it's resolved, GPS navigation will be approved only for supplemental navigation. Integrity is defined as the receiver's ability to detect and flag an unsuitable signal. VORs, localizers and glideslopes achieve this by on-site monitors which automatically shut down the navaid if the signal drifts out of tolerance. Similarly, if the receiver detects a signal anomaly, it will trip the nav flags.

Flagging GPS anomalies is much more complex. As they orbit the earth every 12 hours, GPS satellites receive data uploads from ground stations about every hour, at which time signal integrity is routinely checked. A satellite that's transmitting bad data will be flagged with an unhealthy code which will automatically warn the receiver not to use that satellite for a navigation solution.

To meet IFR en route and non-precision approach specs, however, one hour flagging isn't good enough. For en route approval, the receiver has to flag a faulty nav solution within 30 seconds; for non-precision approaches, it has to meet a 10-second integrity requirement.

The new TSO requires receivers to do this through a technique called Receiver Autonomous Integrity Monitoring (RAIM). RAIM works by "overdetermining" the navigation solution by using more than the minimum number of satellites for a simple three-dimensional position fix. It's sort of like using an extra radial or two when triangulating position from several VORs.

For a RAIM check to detect a questionable solution, the receiver has to have five satellites in view. With six in view, it can determine which satellite is transmitting bad information.

RAIM is a proven method and it's relatively simple to write the required software into a receiver. However, as veteran GPS users are finding out, it's not unusual for just three or four satellites to be in view for many minutes at a time, which is too few for RAIM. Coverage will improve with the full constellation but there will still "RAIM holes" for the foreseeable future.

When you're in a RAIM gap—and there will be a lot of them—you may have perfectly accurate GPS navigation, but without the ability to overdetermine, the receiver won't be able insure integrity. That means that the GPS is temporarily unsuitable for IFR navigation.

Obviously, if you plan to navigate via GPS, it would be nice to know ahead of time if the system is going to be available for an approach when you arrive at your destination. To a certain extent, the TSO allows for this. It requires receivers to have a "look-ahead" feature to calculate RAIM availability within 15 minutes of proposed ETA. No RAIM means no GPS approach.

As GPS advances, we expect to see other integrity methods, including a GPS Integrity Channel (GIC) that transmits integrity data via a devoted satellite downlink, directly to the receiver. GIC is already available in limited form in parts of North America to users of certain communications satellite services.

Approaches ahoy

The certification of the two approach procedures in Colorado completed the first phase of a three-part plan designed to bring satellite navigation on-line for air carriers. The second and third phases involve development and certification of Differential GPS (DGPS) equipment that would allow precision approaches at the two Colorado airports. This is expected within two or three years.

The feds have funded a number of research projects for precision and non-precision approaches. This first phase is the result of a program called GPS overlay.

As its title suggests, the overlay program simply uses existing VOR approaches as the template for the first GPS approaches. Aircraft equipped with certified GPS receivers will be able to simply call up an existing VOR approach and fly it as depicted. The plate itself won't be any different but the receiver database will have the necessary approach fixes defined as waypoints. All together, there are about 4500 approaches that could qualify for overlay. For integrity, the pilot will rely on the underlying VOR approach; RAIM won't be required. If the the underlying approach is notam'd OTS, so is the GPS version.

When Phase II begins, aircraft with RAIM-capable receivers will be able to fly approaches solely with GPS; no VOR back-up required. The FAA says Phase II won't be approved until the military completes the GPS constellation and declares FOC. When Phase III gets underway—1995 at the soonest but possibly later—the FAA will start designing GPS-only approaches. Many of those new procedures will be at airports with existing approaches but at least some will open up outlying airports to IFR operations.

As part of the program, the FAA and other agencies have conducted a number of test programs to prove that GPS is actually capable of providing usable non-precision approach information. One took place in late 1992 at the FAA's Atlantic City Technical Center. A Bonanza A-36 provided by AOPA was used to fly a series of non-precision GPS approaches, using a Northstar receiver. Data from that test and others will be used to develop a GPS chapter for TERPs, the basic blueprint for designing approaches.

How useful?

GPS is touted as being many times more accurate than VOR so you have to wonder about the advantage of having VOR serve as the benchmark for integrity. It's like calibrating a micrometer with a wooden yardstick. Consider this, however: Many airports are miles from the VOR that provides course guidance for the approach. Since VOR accuracy degrades with distance from the navaid, the farther the airport is from the VOR, the larger the obstacle clearance area has to be. And a larger obstacle trapezoid invariably encompasses more towers, trees and mountains, which result in higher minimums.

Initially, GPS won't reduce the minimums but improved course guidance will certainly get you closer to the airport. On a marginal day, that can be the difference between getting in and missing the approach. As GPS progresses and stand-alone approaches become a reality, the obstacle trapezoids will shrink, meaning that lower minimums will be possible.

But don't look to GPS to fulfill loran's failed promise entirely, at least when it comes to approaches. While it is true that earth-reference navigation eliminates the need to have surface navaids within a certain distance of the runway, it's also true that many airports don't have approaches because they're located in a forest of obstacles. Even GPS won't be able to reverse years of airport-hostile zoning laws.

Further, many runways don't have the necessary markings or lighting for instrument operations and some airport operators would rather not be saddled with the liability of having an approach. For years, the FAA has talked about "point-in-space" approaches that would allow pilots to descend to fairly high minimums beneath an overcast in hopes of having enough visibility to see the airport and land. GPS is ideally suited to point-in-space procedures; it remains to be seen if anyone wants them.

Precision approaches, too

One of the most enticing aspects of GPS approaches is the prospect of having precision approaches at smaller airports. Many of these airports don't have obstacle headaches so they already have non-precision procedures and the necessary runway markings and lighting. They simply can't afford full-blown ILSs, which, these days, start at $500,000.

Doubts still exist about GPS's capability as precision navaid but, as research marches on, it appears ever more certain that the GPS-ILS is just around the corner. In 1992, Trimble provided the FAA's Technical Center in Atlantic City with a prototype GPS-ILS system based on differential GPS.

As you may have read, a differential GPS receiver evaluates the ranging data broadcast by the satellites in view. Since it knows its own position with great accuracy, it can correct the system's inherent clock errors and eliminate most of the effects of selective availability, the military's intentional degradation of GPS accuracy. The receiver then broadcasts differential correction to airborne receivers, via a VHF datalink.

Trimble's test system consisted of one of its survey receivers connected to a computer that transmits corrections through an antenna on the roof of a hangar. The FAA's initial tests at Atlantic City suggest that differential is easily accurate enough for Cat I ILSs, even with selective availability in place.

How about Cat II and Cat III ILSs? The airlines are intensely interested in these, both as a foil to the MLS system (which they don't want) and because GPS, when combined with FMS and inertial systems, promises a complete navigation system in a single box. Even GPS's most ardent supporters have expressed doubt that space-based nav will be accurate enough for Cat II and Cat III procedures anytime soon. Yet, as soon as some cynic (or maybe a realist) says it can't be done, someone proves just the opposite.

NASA is conducting a research project through the University of Ohio that suggests that Cat II and Cat III approaches will be possible with GPS. The researchers are using a technique called carrier tracking, which, in simple terms, measures Doppler shift of the satellite signals to produce solutions accurate to within a few centimeters. This technique has long been used in GPS survey receivers which occupy the same site for many minutes. Few thought it would be practical or even possible in moving airplanes.

It turns out, however, that with enough processing power (a 486 notebook, to be precise) carrier tracking is doable and initial tests in a Piper Saratoga demonstrated accuracies within the noise level of the optical tracking device used as ground truth for the tests. Serious questions remain about the robustness of a carrier-tracking Cat II or III system, but the concept is sound.

What it all means

Only a hopeless optimist would suggest that precision approaches will be available to GA aircraft within the next two years but on the other hand, given how fast GPS is moving, we wouldn't rule out anything.

GPS's astonishing advance still doesn't clarify the dilemma over whether to buy loran or GPS, if you're in the upgrade market right now. The manufacturers tell us that there's a strong shift away from loran and toward GPS but the fact is, in North America, loran remains a slightly more capable system. It's comparable in accuracy to GPS, doesn't suffer as many outages and feature-for-feature, panel-mounted loran is cheaper than GPS. As the constellation matures, GPS should get more reliable. But as we said, for VFR use, loran is still the cheaper way to go, all things considered. The Coast Guard won't be pulling the plug on the system for the foreseeable future.

If an IFR-certified, database area navigation system is your wish, we think it's wise to wait another six months to a year. The first round of certified GPS receivers will probably be priced in $5000 to $7000 range. Pricey, to be sure, but capable, too. They'll have full databases plus approach approval. Also, by then, the loran approach program may finally get off the ground and there may be some interesting developments in that field, perhaps in the form of approach-certified loran or multi-sensor units.

For pilots hot to buy GPS right away, ask the manufacturer if the receiver you're interested in can be retrofitted to meet IFR certification requirements. If it can't, you'll be stuck with a VFR box with no approach capability.

• Section Three •

Chart
and
Plate
Briefing

Flight Planning Charts

T here are many resources an IFR pilot has available that can simplify the process of preflight planning. Unfortunately, many of us don't take advantage of them despite the fact that they can save us time and headaches.

A prime example is the flight planning chart. Jeppesen provides one as part of its service. NOS users, however, have to order it separately. Many pilots don't even know it exists, but it can be a handy thing to have.

Planning Products

For pilots who don't have much patience for chart detail, planning a long IFR trip is about as exciting as watching paint dry. Even if you're in no particular hurry, poring over the U.S. LOs in search of a route that'll make ATC's computer happy hardly counts as one of aviation's most inspiring experiences. Then again, a half hour of tedium is certainly preferable to the alternatives: a lost flight plan; fuel exhaustion; a weather briefing for the wrong airport.

Thankfully, both NOS and Jeppesen long ago recognized that pilots need charts dedicated solely to IFR route planning and both publish products intended for that purpose. Curiously, although both services publish excellent planning products, many IFR pilots we know simply don't know about them or don't use them.

This is partly a consequence of contemporary instrument training, which tends to focus more on airwork and flying local approaches than on planning and working the system. We've never heard of an examiner, for example, asking a student to explain how the planning charts should be used.

We generally favor Jeppesen charts, both for planning and enroute, but the NOS products are certainly adequate. Jeppesen subscribers are provided with planning charts as part of any regular subscription (coverage of any region includes a planning chart for the entire U.S.) while NOS users must order the planning charts separately, which may explain why so few pilots use them.

In both cases, the planning charts provide the big picture. The idea is to use them to select both a route and enough reporting stations to determine weather along way, without having to dig out three or four enroute charts, plus plates or an A/FD to look up identifiers. The planning charts depict enough designated airways for filing a flight plan but they are not intended for navigation.

For low-altitude IFR planning, Jeppesen's premier chart is the US (FP/LO). It covers the entire U.S. On the front of the chart, all principal U.S. airways are depicted, along with mileage between fixes formed by navaids. Because the chart doesn't have room for all the airways, the emphasis is on including the longest segments with the fewest route breaks. MEAs are not depicted, although routes with MEAs above 12,500 feet are shown as dashed lines.

For trips of any length, we've found it most useful to select an ATC-acceptable route from the planning chart or, if it's more convenient, we'll look up the preferred route in the A/FD or Jeppesen directory. Once that's done, flip the chart over for a detailed listing, in map and tabular form, of all U.S. weather reporting stations.

This information is really indispensable if you're self-briefing via DUAT or one of the other on line weather services. Over an unfamiliar route, most of us don't know which stations report weather nor do we know which stations take upper air soundings. There's no point in asking for winds aloft for Dayton only to have DUAT respond with "DAY doesn't report FD."

Having the chart handy reduces guesswork, making it less likely that you'll miss something important. True, a DUAT route briefing is supposed to do this automatically but if there's icing or other unusual weather, you may want more than DUAT offers. (One minor oversight: the FP/LO doesn't list NWS radar-site identifiers. Look them up in the A/FD or J-Aid)

If your domestic code reading is a little rusty, the FP/LO has a legend explaining how to read an SA, along with the weather and obstruction to vision symbols, some of which us middle-aged types can't be expected to remember for more than 30 seconds. (Oh sure, T+ is easy enough, but what's -IPW mean?)

The back of the FP/LO also has a road-atlas style mileage table between semi-major cities. These are great circle routes, not airways, but they're adequate for crude time estimates. Other features include an FAA flight-plan form and a listing of the equipment-code designators.

Although we said the FP/LO isn't intended for navigation, it does have one feature that we find very useful while enroute: It's a map showing the areas of coverage for Enroute Flight Advisory Service— better know as Flight Watch. By referring to this map, you'll know to call Leesburg or Charleston or Denver Flight Watch instead of transmitting a to-whom-it-may-concern query that two or three stations answer, yielding an unreadable squeal but no weather.

The planning chart has nine over-sized panels that are far too cumbersome to fold open in the cockpit. However, Jeppesen has cleverly positioned the EFAS map (and the other maps as well) so it can be folded and read as just one panel. During thunderstorm season, or when calls to Flight Watch are frequent, we keep the folded EFAS map clipped under an enroute chart. Also, save the last out-of-date FP/LO and keep it near your briefing computer. The station identifier information rarely changes. Having the chart handy simplifies even local briefings and acts as a checklist, so you don't forget anything important.

For pilots who fly in the flight levels, Jeppesen's FP/HI covers the jet routes. It includes much of the same information found on the FP/LO. Since direct RNAV or inertial routing is fairly common at higher altitudes, the FP/HI lists frequency, class and lat-lon coordinates for principle navaids. It also has weather-briefing information, although it's not as detailed.

The government takes a different approach to planning charts. NOS sells what it calls a Flight Case Planning Chart, which is issued every six months. Like Jeppesen's FP/LO, it depicts principle airways and navaids and has airport listings with mileage tables. NOS used to offer a high-altitude version of this planning chart but it's been discontinued.

Another nice NOS product that was recently discontinued is the giant IFR wall-planning chart you often see tacked on the wall in airport lobbies. This chart covered the entire U.S. in two 40 in. by 50 in. panels. As we went to press, the NOS was considering reintroducing this chart.

The Flight Case Planning Chart contains much of the same information found on the Jeppesen FP/LO, but it's larger, having 11 panels instead of 9. Compared to the Jeppesen chart, the NOS has quite a bit more detail, some of which is useful, some not. Obviously, for planning purposes, you need airway designators, restricted areas and MOAs. Less useful for IFR planning are the chart's inclusion of public-use airports with either an approach or 3000 feet or more of hard-surfaced runway. These just add to the general clutter.

The flight case planner isn't much help in self-briefing. Only VOR identifiers are given, not weather reporting stations. You'll need a copy of AC-045C or a DUAT guide to determine which stations report SAs, FTs and FDs. For EFAS and radar-site identifiers, you'll want a copy of the A/FD for each region you'll be flying in.

If it sounds like planning is more cumbersome with NOS products, we think that is indeed the case. Although we always carry the the A/FDs because we find them easier to use in flight than Jeppesen's bulky J-Aid, the FP/LO is really a one-document flight planner.

Worth a mention are the military's Area Planning Charts, available from the Department of Defense through NOS. These depict instrument and visual training routes used by military aircraft. They're not particularly useful for IFR planning but they're fascinating to look at. And if you're droning along at the MEA and a B-52 should suddenly smoke by 3000 feet *below* you, at least you'll know where it came from.

Notams
and the A/FD

U nfortunately, the system of navigation publications we rely on to fly IFR consists of much more
than just the charts and plates. There's also a lot of
other, supporting information that affects how the charts are used.

If all we had to do was carry the current chart and plate book around, life
would be easy. Instead, we need to deal with notams and other published
information in order to be safe and legal.

A lot of that "other" information is found in a book we've already extolled
the virtues of, the Airport/Facility Directory.

Researching the A/FD

The Airport/Facility Directory (A/FD) is not an exciting publication.
If you ask a group of pilots what they use it for, most will tell you it's
for looking up approach control frequencies and runway lengths.
There is, however, much more significant information that should be
reviewed before flying, especially by instrument pilots.

Getting notams from the friendly FSS briefer and going on your
merry way isn't enough. On a recent flight, a friend of ours went to
Norfolk, VA to practice approaches. His preflight briefing revealed no
current notams. When he arrived at Norfolk, he found that the ILS was
the only procedure available. Why? The Norfolk Vortac was out of
service, sort of.

Operating, but unusable

A review of the A/FD for Norfolk told the story. During a normal
preflight, most pilots would probably glance at the listing and move

on. But a closer reading of the information for ORF Vortac shows that the VOR portion is unusable below 10,000' and 268°-285° all altitudes.

The vortac isn't out of service, you just can't use it below 10,000 feet. Therefore, none of the approaches based on that facility can be flown, leaving the ILS only for use. A review of the notam book reveals amendments to the VOR and RNAV approaches, but the reason for the amendments isn't given.

Another, similar incident also comes to mind. We recently got a call from a flight instructor who had an interesting experience trying to figure out if an instrument approach was current. During an instrument cross-country with a student, the instructor asked the student to divert to a different airport than their planned destination as an exercise in emergency planning. After thumbing through the approach charts, the instructor told the student to ask for the NDB approach at their new destination.

"That NDB has been out of service for almost two years," replied the controller. This astounded the instructor, since he didn't remember seeing anything about the NDB procedure in either the current or published notams before departing. They flew another approach and proceeded without incident.

Curiosity got the better of him, so the instructor did some further research after returning home. Sure enough, he found the answer in the Airport/Facility Directory. The listing for the airport with the NDB approach they wanted to use contained the following note: "XYZ NDB out of service indefinitely."

"That really bothered me," lamented the CFI. "What if I had a bona fide emergency and didn't know that procedure wasn't available? I would have figured it out eventually when I didn't get a station ID, but I'm really surprised the government continues to publish the chart."

The bottom line is that there's information in the A/FD that you won't find on the charts *or* in the regular notam listings. This continues to cause great confusion among pilots. You're supposed to brief yourself on all pertinent information prior to a flight, yet many of us aren't even sure where the information can be found, assuming that asking the weather briefer for notams will cover the bases. Sorry, it won't.

We'll cover notams in greater detail later on, but briefly the situation is as follows. A notam remains a notam until one of two things happens: either it is no longer true, or it gets published. "Published" means that it might show up on a chart or plate, or it might appear in—you guessed it—the A/FD.

A lot of information is packed into the A/FD that requires careful reading to find. For example, several sources of weather can be found in the Norfolk listing: the local telephone number for FSS, the remote frequency for Leesburg FSS and Norfolk has a low-level wind shear alerting system.

Part-time facilities

Many air traffic facilities are operated part-time and you should check to avoid a surprise. The listing for Pennington Gap - Lee County Airport, for example, shows that normal radar service is provided by Tri City Approach/Departure Control from 1100 to 0500 UTC. At all other times, service is provided by Atlanta Center. From 0500-1100 UTC, you can expect limited radar vectoring and loss of radar contact early during the approach, so you should expect to fly the entire approach on your own.

The airport listing should also be reviewed for special instructions on airport lighting to avoid surprises during night approaches. We'll cover pilot-controlled lighting in greater detail later in the book.

Check navaids

It's also a good idea to check the navaids along your route. Like the problem with the Norfolk Vortac mentioned earlier, navaids can have standard features that you won't find in the notams. The listing for some VORs will show many unusable parts of both the VOR and the DME at various altitudes and radials. Harrisburg VOR, which we talked about in Section Two, is a good example of this. Without the knowledge that parts of the VOR aren't usable, you might question the reliability of your equipment, when it's the navaid, not your equipment with the problem.

Reviewing navaid listings also indicates the services available. Hazardous In-Flight Weather Advisory Service (Hiwas) is available over some VORs, for example. Hiwas is a continuous broadcast of severe weather forecast alerts, airmets, sigmets, convective sigmets, urgent pireps, etc. Communication with FSS is also available over many VORs by transmitting on 122.1 and listening on the VOR.

Listed by state

The navaid listings are by state. This can be a pain if you're not certain of the facility location. You might have to refer to a sectional chart to find it, since you can't always determine locations from an IFR en route chart.

Other info

After the airport, heliport and seaplane base listings, you'll find the following information in the order listed:

• **Special Notices**—to find items such as landing distances between intersecting runways at controlled airports, special noise abatement procedures, high density airport reservations, U.S. Customs requirements, etc.

• **Regulatory Notices**—summarizes FAR 93 special air traffic rules, patterns and/or airport traffic areas in effect.

• **FAA & NWS telephone numbers**—find toll-free FSS numbers, flight plan fast-file numbers, touch-tone phone briefings, etc.

• **ARTCC frequencies**—lists all center frequencies by sectors as shown on low altitude en route charts.

• **Preferred IFR routes**—to find the routing you'll most likely receive at certain hours of the day.

• **VOR receiver check sites**—includes VOR receiver check points (ground & airborne) and VOR test facilities (VOT).

• **Parachute jumping areas**—where you can expect to find people hitting the silk.

• **Aeronautical chart bulletins**—changes critical to safety of flight since sectional chart was last published, e.g., obstructions, FSS closings, airspace changes, military training routes, etc.

• **Tower en route control**—provides routes and altitudes for flying IFR between approach control facilities, where applicable.

• **Weather radar network**—a graphic depiction of weather radar sites and upper air observing stations. This is especially helpful for finding radar weather reports.

• **Flight Watch outlets**—graphically depicts Flight Watch outlets and times of operation, so you'll know who to call and when.

Check it all

FAR 91.103 requires every pilot in command to become familiar with all available information concerning that flight. Reviewing the A/FD is part of that information, along with getting a complete weather briefing and reviewing all notams (distant, local and published).

It's unfortunate that all the information we need to fly IFR is spread out in so many publications. Yet, ignoring this information can put you and your passengers at risk.

During a recent IFR flight in IMC, some pilots complained to center that they couldn't receive a certain VOR.

The controller replied, "It's notam'd out of service." We were curious to know what publications they had briefed with. An FAA wag summed up the situation, "If it's published, it's the pilot's responsibility to find it!"

One of the biggest sources of confusion among pilots relates to Notices to Airmen. Many of us assume that all notams appear on the weather briefer's screen (not so). Even those that know there are other notams out there either assume they're not really necessary (often true, sometimes not) or aren't exactly sure how to go about finding them.

There's good news and bad news about notams. The good news is that the FAA undertook a review of the system a few years back and found a lot wrong with it, which indicates that there's hope for change. The bad news is that little has been done yet (not really surprising). We'll talk about the review more later on and describe some of the changes made, but first, here's a look at how the system works.

Notams: The Information Maze

All pilots are familiar with Notices to Airmen (notams)—those unusual conditions passed along by FSS specialists during weather briefings or sometimes tacked onto the end of an ATIS broadcast.

But there's more to the notam system than meets the eye (or ear). Relatively few pilots know how the system works and how to get _all_ the information that may bear on the safety of a flight. A vital bit of information that goes unchecked can lead to an unpleasant surprise— or an accident.

Channeling the flood

All notams are important, whether they are notes about a crane being erected near the end of a runway, a VOR frequency change or an airport abandonment.

The trouble is that there are so many of them. If pilots had to wade through all of them to get to the tidbits relating to their flight plans, they'd never get off the ground. To channel the vast flood of information into more usable streams, the FAA breaks notams down into three categories: distant (D), local (L) and Flight Data Center (FDC).

Notams also are divided into two separate classes that indicate the form in which they are available. These used to be called Class I and Class II. FAA has since dropped the name, but the distinction remains. The first kind of notam (was Class I) is one that has yet to be published—in other words, it's available on-line, and the other kind (was Class II) is a notam that has been published in the biweekly Notices to Airmen bulletin.

What's the difference?

D notams can be thought of as the "big time." They deal with critical information such as airport closures, frequency changes, anything having to do with navaids and anything that might affect an instrument approach. D notams contain information that could affect a pilot's decision on whether to make a flight. They're automatically attached to the hourly weather reports.

L notams are, for the most part, less critical and contain "nice-to-know" information, such as taxiway closures. They don't appear on hourly weather reports and are kept in a separate file at the FSS.

FDC notams are another animal entirely—they come from the National Flight Data Center, which is responsible for the structure of the nation's airspace. These notams cover such things as changes to airways and instrument approach procedures.

What you get

So, what exactly is the pilot getting when the briefer reads "the notams?" *Not* necessarily what you might expect: the entire list of notams—L, D and FDC. The list would probably be too lengthy to be much use, and much of the information wouldn't be particularly useful in the first place. A VFR pilot launching on a clear day probably doesn't need to know about an ILS procedure change. Nor is he likely to care one way or the other.

Class comparison

As we noted above, all notams break down into two classes. Notams that are still being distributed electronically to the FSS remain on the system one of two things happens: It gets published somewhere, or the situation that called for it no longer exists. When it gets published in the Notices to Airmen it drops off-line.

It is important to know that when a notam disappears, it either is no longer valid or has become permanent. NASA's Aviation Safety Report System bulletin, *Callback*, included a report a few years back that illustrates the sort of trouble a pilot can get into if this is not kept in mind. The report was from a pilot who noticed that a notam for inoperative runway lights at his destination had been dropped from his computer-service printout. He assumed that the lights had been fixed and proceeded to fly an instrument approach down to the minimums that apply when the approach lights are working. In fact, the minimums were higher because the lights were still out of service (and had been for the past two years). The catch was that the information had been published, and so was no longer being distributed electronically. He would have discovered that if he had checked the A/FD, the notams section of his Jepp charts, or the Notices to Airmen.

A notam is first published in the Notices to Airmen book, which is part of the Airman's Information Manual (AIM). From there, depending on the type of information, it might go into the A/FD or onto a chart or approach plate. Or it might disappear. Notams that aren't expected to last more than a week never get published; those that aren't expected to become permanent stay in the notams book. There are also special notices that don't really belong anywhere else, like special flight restrictions over a presidential inauguration or the special flight rules for the EAA convention in Oshkosh.

The rub

Notams that aren't on-line but are still in effect are found in the notam book. But who has the book? It's not something you'll find in every flight bag. We called several local FBOs, and none subscribe to the bulletin. Of course, it's kept at FSSs, but gone are the days when most pilots live near one.

As far as FAA is concerned, there's no excuse for missing a notam published in the book. As we've seen, "checking notams" with Flight Service or a computer system can leave a pilot short. Of course, anyone may get a subscription to the notams book from the Government Printing Office, Superintendent of Documents, Washington, D.C. 20402. But it's costly.

Getting what's needed

In most cases, notams provided by a briefer are all that's needed. At an automated FSS, a briefer simply punches the planned route of flight into his computer and gets, among many other things, D and FDC notams from stations within 50 miles either side of the route. (Briefers in non-automated FSSs have to take a few extra steps to get FDC notams.)

A specialist is required to provide notam information *only* during a "full" weather briefing. If a pilot requests an abbreviated briefing or already is airborne, he or she will have to specifically ask for notams if they want them. Further, the briefer has the discretion to give only the information that is obviously applicable to the route of flight. That final edit is where the briefer's expertise comes into play. L notams are kept separately, either in a book or in a separate computer listing at a few FSSs.

In the likely event the pilot doesn't have the Notices to Airmen book available, the briefer will read the published notams if asked—but only if asked. Most of the time, the published notams won't be of all that much interest—nearly all of them are FDC notams, and the situation is rare that being unaware of an FDC notam will make a real difference. But occasionally an important D notam will turn up in the published listings and nowhere else. It pays to check.

It also pays to keep on hand a *current* copy of the ultimate repository of most notam information—the A/FD. Many pilots eschew it for commercial airport guides that are easier to read. But, there's a lot of valuable information in the A/FD that doesn't appear in the commecial guides.

Ripples in the flow

By and large, the notam system serves us well, providing one knows how it works and how to make good use of it. But there are situations in which human error or heavy traffic can take their toll on the accuracy of notam information.

D and L notams originate when someone at the affected facility calls the local FSS on a special line and talks with a specialist whose sole function is to handle notam listings. In the case of a D notam, the specialist enters it into the national database, where all FSSs can see it. An example of a D notam would be an airport manager calling to say that the airport has closed because of severe weather.

L notams, on the other hand, are recorded in a book. This would be something like noting that the taxiway lights on one side of the airport are out due to construction.

Similarly, when the condition that created the notam changes, the facility calls the FSS and the specialist takes the notam out of the system. (FDC notams are transmitted to the FSS from the National Flight Data Center, itself, and are logged in a book.)

Every two weeks, the notam specialist goes through the book and removes from the system all the notams that have been published. (Notams automatically go into the book after a fixed period of time on-line.)

When activity gets heavy—during a snowstorm, for instance, when every airport in the region is closing runways for snow removal—the notam specialist can easily get swamped and the information that finally does get onto the notam list may no longer be valid. Also, clerical errors occasionally find their way into the system, but not often.

While dated information isn't often found on the D notam list, an L notam can easily be kept around long after it's no longer valid. That's because it's up to the facility that originated the notam to let the FSS know it's no longer in effect, and people sometimes forget. With D notams, the FSS will call the facility back to follow up on the notam.

Another way a potentially useful bit of information could get lost is in the briefing, itself. Since briefers don't read all notams applicable to the route (it would be neither practical nor desirable to do so—there are simply too many), they provide a filter for what pilots actually learn.

There are a few areas where the notam system has been tweaked to make it a bit better. In the northeast, for example, there is a letter of agreement between the Bridgeport, Burlington and Bangor AFSSs to share L notam information electronically.

Behind the times

While the notam system works, it is a dated way of distributing information. The system was devised 30 years ago around the equipment then in use—teletypes. Given that the computer technology in common use today was unheard of then, the capability of the hardware has far outstripped the procedures in place.

Accordingly, FAA decided a few years back to review the entire system to see how it might be streamlined and made more efficient. We'll talk about some of the findings in the following pages.

In the meantime, pilots can make their travels a bit safer and even more convenient by being sure to check the notams—all of them.

As we noted above, the FAA undertook a review of the notam system a few years back, and (surprise!) found it lacking. Some big changes were proposed to make it simpler, but none of these have been adopted as yet. Some of the lesser changes were made, however, so while still cumbersome, the notam system is a bit better than it had been.

FAA's Notam Review

Just as there are two kinds of retractable gear pilots, so too are there two kinds of instrument pilots: those who have the patience to get a thorough preflight briefing and those who don't.

We suspect that a fair number of pilots, if not the majority, are in the latter group. One reason for this is that it's easy to fall into the bad habit of the abbreviated briefing. It doesn't take much experience to learn that you can usually cut corners during a briefing and not suffer any consequences. If you're in a hurry and the weather's not that bad or you're flying over a familiar route, why bother inquiring about an extra alternate or slogging through the area forecast? Most of the time, you can get by without it.

Jeppesen and DUAT:
Best for Notams

Unless you're a notams expert, it's hard to know if you've got all the pertinent notams for a proposed flight. Most of the time, it doesn't much matter if you miss a notam. Occasionally, however, being unaware of a notam might prove hazardous or, if you're lucky, just embarrassing.

For the Class Is, we think DUAT is the best free source, though some of the pay-as-you-go services, specifically EMI, offer somewhat better service. As a means of editing irrelevant information, the FSS computer suppresses airport notams along the route of flight. You can certainly ask an FSS briefer to look up the airport notams if you think of it. On DUAT, the notams are provided as part of a route briefing. However, if you want to double check, it's easy to select the appropriate notams files from the A/FD and then search for important airport notams along your route of flight.

For the Class IIs, you could subscribe to Notices to Airman ($79 a year). So long as you keep the subscription current, you'll be as covered as it's possible to get. You might miss a notam that falls between the crack of the Class II's publication date and its removal from the A wire but at least you will have checked every conceivable source. The downside of subscribing to the government's notams is the cost. For equivalent chart and plate coverage, Jeppesen and NOS are very close in cost.

However, Jeppesen subscribers receive notams as part of a regular subscription. Jeppesen's terminal and enroute chart notams are, for all practical purposes, the same as the government's Class II notams. They are also "an accepted substitute" for the official version, as described in the FARs. Jeppesen notams are issued on the service's standard revision cycle. They come as loose sheets which fit into the front of the binder, under the notams tab. When a new revision arrives, you discard the old ones. Whether you have full U.S. coverage or not, you get enroute and terminal notams for the entire U.S., plus overlaping enroute information for Canada, Mexico and the Bahamas.

Jeppesen is pretty quick to incorporate permanent changes into the plates and charts but those that don't make the plate revisions, are listed in the notams sheets.

When time is short and the briefing is hectic, one of the first things tossed overboard is review of the notams. It's easy to understand why this happens. As currently construed, the notam system defies understanding by a person of average intelligence and it often requires an inordinate amount of time to dig up information that ultimately has no bearing on the flight being planned.

For a pilot who knows how to use the system, the introduction of DUAT has improved the quality of a preflight weather briefing while reducing the time required to get it. But DUAT hasn't helped clarify the the notams mess. If anything, it's created more confusion since pilots who had relied on FSS briefers as guides through the notam jungle suddenly had to go it alone.

The FAA, having heard many complaints and little praise for the way it disseminates notams, is not unaware of the situation. In 1990, it undertook a review of the notam system and, not surprisingly, found serious faults.

Nobody knows

The notam review sought comments from everyone who uses the system, including pilots, ATC at all levels, the airlines, the military and FBOs. At the outset, it revealed the obvious: very few people really understand how the notam system is organized or how it's supposed to work. And that includes a fair number of FSS briefers, who most pilots expect to be fairly expert on the subject.

"We found that people just didn't know how find the notams they needed," said Fred Gibbs, an FAA official in the U.S. Notams office.

"We had an airport operator who didn't realize it was his responsibility to report runway notams and he didn't know who he was supposed to call to report them."

If the people who are supposed to originate notams are confused, imagine the poor pilot, whose job it is to ferret the information out of FSS or DUAT. Much of the confusion stems from the Byzantine organization of the notams system.

Pilots did not generally understand, for example, the difference between Class I and Class II notams. As we noted above, Class I notams were those notams posted on the Service A teletype wire and they're what you get when you ask an FSS briefer for notams. If they're of sufficient duration, notams that first appeare on Service A are eventually published in Notices to Airmen, which is issued every 15 days and is available by subscription from the government. Once published, a notam was considered Class II and was removed from Service A. None of that has changed. The FAA simply stopped calling the two kinds of notam Class I and Class II. They now have no name. Instead, they're either on-line or published.

FSS specialists, as part of a standard briefing, do provide on-line notams. It's assumed that the pilot subscribes to the published notams so they are not provided. According to the AIM, FSS will provide the published notams if they are specifically requested but in our experience, the briefer doesn't always have the current notam book handy.

To further confuse the pilot, until recently some notams were available from all FSS sources (notam Ds) while others (notam Ls) were issued only by FSSs in the area where the airport happens to be. Sorting out which is which requires fairly intimate knowledge of the basic notams structure.

Even pilots with a good understanding of the class system and who are methodical enough to ask for all available notams, might yet be foiled by the way FSS and DUAT disseminate information from the notams database. For the sake of brevity, FSS, for example, suppresses airport notams along a given route of flight. Thus, if you asked for notams for a nighttime trip between Cleveland and Chicago and had to stop unexpectedly at Elkhart, Ind., you wouldn't have the notam that the runway lights were OTS, unless you happened to ask for it. Not having the notam, you wrongly assume that airport operations were normal.

New and improved

The FAA's review of the notam system has produced several minor tune-ups and a long list of recommendations now circulating within the agency. None of the major recommendations, have been adopted. More than likely, if they're approved at all, they will be integrated on a piecemeal basis rather than in one instantaneous revision of the system.

First, the tune-ups: As of late 1990, the distinction between notam Ls and notam Ds has been changed. Under the old system, only airports marked with a section or "seahorse" symbol in the A/FD had notam D service. Now, all airports have D service. D and L notams still exist but the classifications relate to how important the information is considered to be. A taxiway closure, for example, rates an L while a runway gets a D notam.

This change avoids a situation that, while rare, could cause real problems on occasion. Previously, since some airports didn't have D notam service, by definition all notams issued about those airports were L notams. An airport could actually be closed, with heavy construction equipment all over the runways, and chances are nobody would catch it unless they thought to check the L notams.

A second change is the dropping of the class designations already mentioned.

Another change relates to parachute jumping notams which are now tied to specific VORs and are issued as fix/radial/distance. Similarly, navaids not part of the route structure are now tied specifically to airport identifiers. So if the ABC NDB is down for maintenance, the notam will tell you which airport is affected. Under the old method, you had to look it up yourself.

Future notams changes may be more far reaching. One recommendation would have a single, standard format for notams; no distinction drawn to FDC notams and no more Ls and Ds, at least as we know them now.

Instead, notams would be provided according to the type and route of flight being conducted, without regard to whether the notams were originated by the Flight Data Center or the Ajax Flying Service.

If you were flying a short VFR hop in daylight, you wouldn't need to know that the ILS and approach light system were out of service. Irrelevant notams, such as the one warning pilots not to transport Ferdinand Marcos' remains back into the Philippines issued a few years back, would have to be specifically requested or would appear in published form.

Under this system, the notam book would be all but done away with. Only the graphs, tables and drawings that might appear in notams would be published in the book. Everything would be available on line, either through FSS via Service A or on DUAT and the contract briefing services. With the dropping of the class designations the notam book did get thinner for a while, but now it's started to bulk up again, so it appears that FAA still hasn't quite settled on how to handle the idea.

There's a relatively new species of notam out there to go along with the Ls, Ds, and FDCs. It's the Chart Change Notam, and was devised to get around a Catch-22 in the regs.

One of the biggest problems with the chart revision/notam system of disseminating information to pilots is the way in which it's scattered about. To actually get to all the important information, it's sometimes necessary to pore over three or four different publications: tedious to the point that few if any of us actually do so.

So, the Chart Change was invented to put some of the more critical revisions where they ought to be: on the plate where they're hard to miss. Although you may not have noticed, NOS plates are a bit more current as a result of these new notams. Here's how they work.

Chart Change Notams

Geez, we hate it when: (a) during an ICC, some pimply faced CFII who really knows his stuff nails us on a diddly plate revision we knew to look for in the notams but were too lazy to check or (b) that new localizer frequency was on the notams printout after all, but we find it only after we've been spanked by approach for not knowing it.

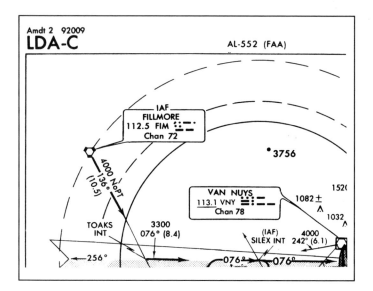

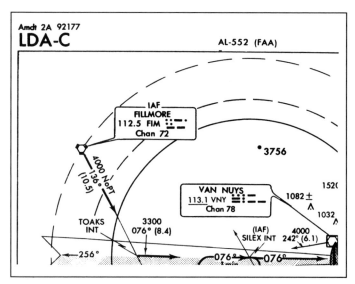

Any of this sound familiar? It ought to. Unless your hobby is collecting trivial government documents, 90 percent of what's in the notams goes unnoticed, meaning that most of us are gross violators of the all available information clause. If you don't get caught unawares at least once or twice a year because of something you missed in the notams, you're trying way too hard.

Over the years, the notams system has gotten so cumbersome that it just about collapsed of its own weight and would have had not some minor but important changes occurred. We discussed some of these above, but there's another specialized notam introduced about a year ago, specifically to improve the currency of NOS plates.

This notam is variously called a CC, a CCP or CCN, depending on who you're talking to. In any case, the CC stands for Chart Change, the P for permanent and/or the N for notam. CC is the important thing to remember, however. To understand how a CCP works and why it's important, you need to know how NOS plates are updated.

NOS products (plates and en routes) are issued on the 56-day airspace cycle, meaning you get a new booklet about every two months. To communicate changes that occur between the 56-day cycles, NOS sends the off-cycle Change Notice 28 days after the start of each airspace cycle. For daily or weekly (or even hourly) changes, notams are posted on Flight Service's Service A wire (and DUAT) and in the biweekly Notices to Airmen publication or what used to be called Class II notams.

In theory, even though this system is clumsy, it does cover all the bases, as long you know where to find the really important stuff. One major flaw, however, is something called a temporary notam or t-notam. T-notams announce changes that are supposed to last for fewer than 120 days; say, for instance, runway construction that temporarily raises the minimums on an ILS. Normally, the t-notam communicating the change would appear first on Service A then, a few weeks later, in the published notams. So far so good.

Unfortunately, airport construction problems have a way of taking four or five times as long as they're supposed to so what starts as a temporary change, becomes semi-permanent. Because the FAA has prohibited NOS from charting t-notams, the original plate—in this case with its erroneous minimums—is published cycle after cycle, sometimes for several years. Using the example above, to find the correct minimums, you'd have to first check the regular NOS booklet, then the Change Notice, then the biweekly Notices to Airman publication followed by the notams you picked off Service A or DUAT. Some system, eh?

Enter the CCP notam. This notam allows NOS to revise the plate with the latest correct data, even though it's only a temporary change. It also permits NOS to issue new plates for certain kinds of revisions that, under the old system, had to be flight checked before being published.

In the example shown here, the LDA-C for Van Nuys—two important changes were made to the approach; an intersection was deleted and circling minimums were revised. Under the old system, this change would have appeared first on Service A, then in the published notams. Before it could appear as a revised plate, the approach had to have been flight checked and reviewed.

By communicating the revision via CCP notam, NOS can chart the revisions and distribute a new plate as soon as practical. The entire process is transparent to users, except for the fact that plates revised via CCP notam have an alpha identifier after the amendment number. In the case of Van Nuys, it's Amdt 2A, while the old plate was designated Amdt 2.

What's it all mean? For Jeppesen users, absolutely nothing. Jeppesen has always issued new plates to reflect t-notams it felt were important. Along with its fortnightly chart revision packages, Jeppesen also sends an edited version of what appears in the Notices to Airman booklet. As we've said before, Jeppesen still recommends that its customers also subscribe to the published notams although, in our experience, very few do.

For NOS users, CCP notams definitely improve the currency of the plates. Yes, you're still supposed to check the Change Notice and both notams sources, but now that important t-notams are being charted, the chances of missing something really critical are greatly reduced. Eventually, we would like to see the published notams done away with entirely but for the time being at least, CCP notams represent real progress.

While Jeppesen recommends that its subscribers also get the Notices to Airmen book (just to be safe and to keep the lawyers happy), the company does provide an edited list of what appears there as part of its regular service.

In many ways, it obviates the need to check the notam book. But, it's not quite the same thing. Here's how it works.

Jeppesen's Chart Notams

Serious students of the FARs soon realize that Part 91 has more than its share of inconsistencies, ill-defined concepts and ridiculous notions. Our vote for the winner in that last category is 91.103, the notorious "all available information" clause. In spirit, this clause is aimed making it a crime to blast off into the blue (or gray) yonder without proper pre-flight preparation.

Fair enough. We think the government *should* try to minimize the number of smoking craters that result from pilots taking off with insufficient fuel or gyros that don't work. The less we alarm the general public, the better. Unfortunately, 91.103 is like a big, tangled ball of yarn. Tug on it long enough and eventually it unravels to reveal a dirty little core called notams.

Notams began as a noble idea but, over the years, they've become a real mess. The notams system is awkward and confusing and we don't know many people who fully understand it. Jeppesen's published notams, which are mailed out every two weeks with its regular revisions, have always done a good job of cutting through the clutter. Beginning with the December 18th, 1992 revision, Jeppesen has restructured its notam service and from what we can tell, the new system is considerably improved.

As we discussed above, there are three categories of notams; Local (Ls), Distant (D) and Flight Data Center (FDC) notams. Notam Ls and Ds appear (mostly) on Flight Service's Service-A and on DUAT. FDC notams—which announce airspace and procedure changes—appear either on those two services or in the twice-monthly Notices to Airmen published by the FAA.

Published notams, that is, those in the booklet, used to be called Class II notams, but that designation has been dropped. You'll still hear the notams booklet called Class II notams, however, so be prepared. The Ls and Ds, by the way, were and often still are called Class I notams.

As we've explained before, users of NOS charts are expected to subscribe to the Notices to Airmen booklet. Since it's issued every two weeks, it's often the only source of important procedural changes that occur between the issuance date of NOS charts and plates, which come out every 56 days. So, to be sure of being absolutely current, NOS users need to check plates, the Change Notice and the notams booklet.

Jeppesen does things a little differently. It sends subscribers revisions every 14 days. These revisions contain new plates and periodically, new en route charts, too. Rather than expecting subscribers to look up any potential changes to a plate in the notams, as NOS users must do, Jeppesen simply incorporates change into new plates and sends them along to subscribers.

Temporary changes of short duration or those that aren't worth incorporating into a new plate right away are listed in a series of separate notam sheets which users are supposed to file in the binder under the notams tab. Every two weeks, subscribers get a new batch of notams. To update, you simply remove the old batch and replace with the new. If there are any special notices or other items of interest, the revision's cover sheet will explain this.

This aspect of Jeppesen's service is probably vastly under appreciated. The company invests enormous effort in its notam service. At Jeppesen's Englewood, Colorado offices, several technicians devote almost all of their time to notams, checking the system on literally an hourly basis. Since Jeppesen's policy is to incorporate important changes as they occur, a pilot with a newly revised Airway Manual is about as current as it's possible to be. Any important data not actually on the newest plates, will appear in the section under the notam tab. Anything any fresher will have to come from FSS or DUAT.

Until recently, Jeppesen notams did have one major flaw: The en route portion of the notams were quite difficult to read. These were were organized alphabetically rather than by state, thus, on a trip of any length, you'd have to plow through the entire section looking for notices about airways, navaids and intersections along your route.

The new-improved notams service retains the two-section format, one section for en route, one for terminal. The en route portion is reorganized into sections on navaids, airport name changes, airways, airspace, off-airways intersections and holding patterns. Within each section, the individual items are arranged alphabetically (for named fixes, airports, etc.) and numerically for airways.

This means for a typical trip, after you've planned your route, you'd look in the en route section first to see if any navaids are notam'd, then on down the line for fixes, airports and airways. This is a tremendous improvement over the old system, which was a confusing jumble of intersections, airways and airports.

En route charts don't change all that much but some changes are definitely worth knowing about. Because Jeppesen issues new en routes only periodically rather than on the 56-day cycle that NOS follows, reviewing the en route notams is worth the 30 seconds it takes to do it.

The terminal notam section, which contains information on specific procedures, frequency changes and so forth will remain organized by state, then alphabetically by airport.

We've always felt that Jeppesen's notam service is complete enough to do the job but—and some may consider this important—it's not identical to the government notam booklet. For one thing, some of the notams in the government booklet will already be charted on Jeppesen plates; no need to look up the changes. Second, because Jeppesen's revision dates don't correspond to the publication of the government's notam booklet, it's possible that a small number of notams will slip between the cracks.

However, if you're doing a thorough job of pre-flight briefing, you should pick these up from FSS or DUAT. Keep this in mind, too: Flight Service Stations have the twice-monthly notams booklet. If you want to review its contents for the flight at hand, you'll have to either visit the FSS in person or make a point to ask the specialist to locate the booklet. Again, the old hands may call it the Class II notams but you'll know what they're talking about.

SIDs
and STARs

Among the most complex of charts an IFR pilot has to deal with are Standard Instrument Departures (SIDs) and Standard Terminal Arrivals (STARs). *Fortunately, a little study usually reveals that the routings and instructions depicted on them aren't really all that complicated: they only seem that way because of the visual clutter.*

Until a few years ago, Jepp users had a distinct advantage of NOS customers because the SIDs and STARs are kept in Jepp binders with the approach plates for the airport. NOS users had to subscribe to two additional books (three if full U.S. coverage was desired) that contained nothing but SIDs and STARs.

Now, however, NOS has seen the light, listened to the pilots, and is publishing the SIDs and STARs right along with the rest of the plates. For some reason, though, the STARs are put at the front of the book, while the SIDs are paired with their airports.

Jepp users still have a bit of an edge, however, in that the Jeppesen format allows for fold-out charts with more surface area for those really complex procedures.

First we'll cover how to fly SIDs, then we'll pick apart a couple of them to illustrate how best to deal with these beasts.

Flying the SID

Much of the workload in flight operations occurs during the instrument departure. Immediately after takeoff, you are thrust into the realm of scanning, navigation and air traffic control. The pressure of the transition can be increased by turbulence, icing, or vertigo. Think back and we're sure you will agree that some of the most harrowing moments in your flying occurred in the first few minutes of entering instrument meteorological conditions.

The FAA establishes standard instrument departures (SIDs) and IFR departure procedures to assist you when departing on instruments. SIDs are coded departure instructions that expedite the clearance delivery process. IFR departure procedures are established solely for obstacle clearance during an instrument takeoff.

Richard Taylor, in his book *Instrument Flying*, refers to SIDs as "short range preferred routes." You can file a SID to prevent extensive clearance copying and to avoid a hassle from ATC.

Less writing

To demonstrate how a SID reduces copying clearances, refer to the Gnats One Departure for Medford, Oregon. Assume you have filed an IFR flight plan from Medford to Eugene, Oregon via Victor 23 (which is the 333 degree radial from OED VOR). Your clearance will probably be as follows: "ATC clears N54321 to the Eugene Airport via Gnats One Departure, Mourn Transition then as filed, climb and maintain 8,000, squawk 0400."

If you don't have the SID, the controller must issue a complicated clearance with radial crossing restrictions, since you must climb to clear mountainous terrain and avoid incoming traffic.

The clearance in this example would be: "ATC clears N54321 to the Eugene Airport via after departure, turn right direct Viole, thence via the Viole 270 degree bearing to Merli intersection. Proceed on the Medford 15 DME arc to intercept the Medford 333 degree radial to Mourn, then as filed. Climb and maintain 8,000, cross Gnats at or above 4,100. Departure control frequency will be 124.3, squawk 0400."

The textual descriptions of transitions on SID charts can be intimidating by turning the chart into a sea of fine print. A transition is simply a variation in the procedure to increase the flexibility of the SID for aircraft heading out in different directions. Take time to examine both the graphic depiction and the text itself. Otherwise, you may miss an important detail or set the OBS to an incorrect radial. Often the text will clarify the graphic and vice versa. Use a highlighter pen to mark the transition assigned for your route of flight.

Pilot Nav or Vector

The two types of SIDs used by air traffic control are known as Pilot Nav and Vector SIDs. During a Pilot Nav SID, such as the Gnats One Departure, the pilot is responsible for navigating and maintaining the appropriate altitude. The Hobby Seven Departure is a Vector SID,

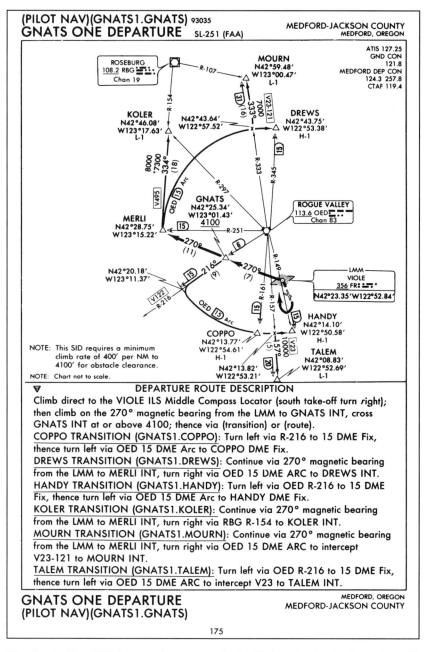

(PILOT NAV)(GNATS1.GNATS) 93035
GNATS ONE DEPARTURE   SL-251 (FAA)

MEDFORD-JACKSON COUNTY
MEDFORD, OREGON

ATIS 127.25
GND CON
121.8
MEDFORD DEP CON
124.3 257.8
CTAF 119.4

ROSEBURG
108.2 RBG
Chan 19

MOURN
N42°59.48'
W123°00.47'
L-1

R-107

KOLER
N42°46.08'
W123°17.63'
L-1

N42°43.64'
W122°57.52'

DREWS
N42°43.75'
W122°53.38'
H-1

MERLI
N42°28.75'
W123°15.22'

GNATS
N42°25.34'
W123°01.43'
4100

ROGUE VALLEY
113.6 OED
Chan 83

N42°20.18'
W123°11.37'

270°
(11)

270°
(7)

LMM
VIOLE
356 FR
N42°23.35'W122°52.84'

COPPO
N42°13.77'
W122°54.61'
H-1

HANDY
N42°14.10'
W122°50.58'
H-1

TALEM
N42°08.83'
W122°52.69'
L-1

N42°13.82'
W122°53.21'

NOTE: This SID requires a minimum
climb rate of 400' per NM to
4100' for obstacle clearance.

NOTE: Chart not to scale.

DEPARTURE ROUTE DESCRIPTION

Climb direct to the VIOLE ILS Middle Compass Locator (south take-off turn *right*);
then climb on the 270° magnetic bearing from the LMM to GNATS INT, cross
GNATS INT at or above 4100; thence via (transition) or (route).
COPPO TRANSITION (GNATS1.COPPO): Turn left via R-216 to 15 DME Fix,
thence turn left via OED 15 DME Arc to COPPO DME Fix.
DREWS TRANSITION (GNATS1.DREWS): Continue via 270° magnetic bearing
from the LMM to MERLI INT, turn right via OED 15 DME ARC to DREWS INT.
HANDY TRANSITION (GNATS1.HANDY): Turn left via OED R-216 to 15 DME
Fix, thence turn left via OED 15 DME Arc to HANDY DME Fix.
KOLER TRANSITION (GNATS1.KOLER): Continue via 270° magnetic bearing
from the LMM to MERLI INT, turn right via RBG R-154 to KOLER INT.
MOURN TRANSITION (GNATS1.MOURN): Continue via 270° magnetic bearing
from the LMM to MERLI INT, turn right via OED 15 DME ARC to intercept
V23-121 to MOURN INT.
TALEM TRANSITION (GNATS1.TALEM): Turn left via OED R-216 to 15 DME Fix,
thence turn left via OED 15 DME ARC to intercept V23 to TALEM INT.

GNATS ONE DEPARTURE
(PILOT NAV)(GNATS1.GNATS)

MEDFORD, OREGON
MEDFORD-JACKSON COUNTY

175

*The Gnats One SID is a good example of why SIDs exist in the first place. If
ATC had to issue the complex routings required to all departing IFR aircraft
they'd never get anything done.*

during which the controller provides obstacle clearance.

A clearance for a flight from Houston Hobby to New Orleans could be the following: "ATC clears N54321 to the New Orleans Airport via Hobby Seven Departure, Beaumont, then flight planned route. Climb and maintain 3,000, expect 9,000 10 minutes after departure." No departure control frequency is mentioned.

The SID depicts three communication sectors. In this procedure, the Beaumont VOR lies in the north and east sector, so you would contact Houston Hobby Departure Control on 119.7. Flying westbound towards Austin, the frequency is 123.8; when southbound, contact the controller on 134.45.

This is a good time to mention that some SIDs contain lost communication procedures in the event that you cannot contact ATC soon after takeoff. When established on a transition or major part of the SID, proceed with your last assigned clearance and continue the flight. Planning for this emergency is another good reason for thoroughly reviewing the SID procedure while on the ground.

Satellite airports also use SIDs

You could also be assigned the Hobby Seven Departure when departing from an airport in the Houston area other than Hobby. On Jeppesen charts, there's a block in the corner of the chart entitled "Airports Served." This indicates where you can expect to be given the SID.

The notation in parenthesis above the Hobby Seven Departure (HUB7.HUB) is for FAA use when entering the SID into the ATC computer. You should use this abbreviation along with the first en route fix if you wish to use the SID when filing an IFR flight plan by requesting your route as "HUB7.BPT, V222 LCH, V20 MSY."

Although SIDs are used primarily to reduce the time and aggravation of clearance copying, these procedures can also protect you from obstacles and terrain when departing. The FAA also establishes IFR departure procedures at airports solely for obstacle clearance.

IFR departure procedures

An IFR departure procedure is *not* the same thing as a SID. As we noted above, SIDs exist primarily to make life easier for both ATC and pilots by, in effect, informing the pilot ahead of time of the route he'll be given anyway. A departure procedure exists for an entirely different reason: to ensure obstacle clearance.

Many pilots and not a few FSS specialists are confused on this issue. There was one high-profile accident a few years ago that killed country singer Reba McEntire's band when the flight crew of a chartered

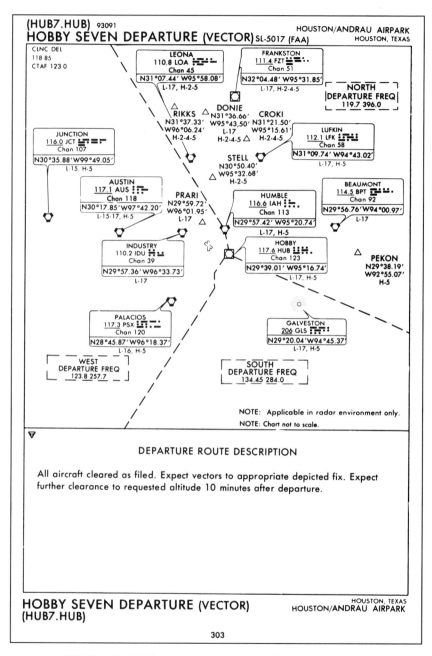

(HUB7.HUB) 93091
HOBBY SEVEN DEPARTURE (VECTOR) SL-5017 (FAA)
HOUSTON/ANDRAU AIRPARK
HOUSTON, TEXAS

CLNC DEL
118 85
CTAF 123 0

LEONA
110.8 LOA
Chan 45
N31°07.44' W95°58.08'
L-17, H-2-5

FRANKSTON
111.4 FZT
Chan 51
N32°04.48' W95°31.85'
L-17, H-2-4-5

NORTH
DEPARTURE FREQ
119.7 396.0

DONIE
N31°36.66'
RIKKS
N31°37.33'
W96°06.24'
H-2-4-5
W95°43.50'
L-17
H-2-4-5
CROKI
N31°21.50'
W95°15.61'
H-2-4-5

LUFKIN
112.1 LFK
Chan 58
N31°09.74' W94°43.02'
L-17, H-5

JUNCTION
116.0 JCT
Chan 107
N30°35.88' W99°49.05'
L-15, H-5

STELL
N30°50.40'
W95°32.68'
H-2-5

AUSTIN
117.1 AUS
Chan 118
N30°17.85' W97°42.20'
L-15-17, H-5

PRARI
N29°59.72'
W96°01.95'
L-17

HUMBLE
116.6 IAH
Chan 113
N29°57.42' W95°20.74'
L-17, H-5

BEAUMONT
114.5 BPT
Chan 92
N29°56.76' W94°00.97'
L-17

INDUSTRY
110.2 IDU
Chan 39
N29°57.36' W96°33.73'
L-17

HOBBY
117.6 HUB
Chan 123
N29°39.01' W95°16.74'
L-17, H-5

PEKON
N29°38.19'
W92°55.07'
H-5

PALACIOS
117.3 PSX
Chan 120
N28°45.87' W96°18.37'
L-16, H-5

GALVESTON
206 GLS
N29°20.04' W94°45.37'
L-17, H-5

WEST
DEPARTURE FREQ
123.8 257.7

SOUTH
DEPARTURE FREQ
134.45 284.0

NOTE: Applicable in radar environment only.
NOTE: Chart not to scale.

DEPARTURE ROUTE DESCRIPTION

All aircraft cleared as filed. Expect vectors to appropriate depicted fix. Expect
further clearance to requested altitude 10 minutes after departure.

HOBBY SEVEN DEPARTURE (VECTOR)
(HUB7.HUB)
HOUSTON, TEXAS
HOUSTON/ANDRAU AIRPARK

303

*A vector SID like the Hobby Seven is a bit simpler to read than a pilot nav
procedure. Essentially, it gives you some very basic instructions, and you leave
the rest to ATC.*

Hawker-Siddely jet couldn't get the difference between the two sorted out and crashed into the mountains near San Diego.

The criteria FAA uses for obstacle and terrain clearance is published in the TERPS manual. It requires that an obstacle clearance plane with a 40:1 slope be established from the end of each runway. All obstacles and terrain within the immediate vicinity of the airport are evaluated. If an obstacle penetrates the 40:1 plane, an IFR departure procedure is established so the pilot can avoid the obstacle during an instrument takeoff.

IFR departure procedures are listed on the lower portion of the airport diagram page on Jeppesen charts, and published in the front of NOS approach volumes. A T symbol in an inverted black triangle, found in the lower left hand corner of NOS approach charts alerts you to the presence of departure procedures or takeoff minimums.

Climb gradients

When following an IFR departure procedure, you must be able to climb at least 200 feet per nautical mile unless otherwise noted. The procedure provides at least 48 feet of clearance per nautical mile above any obstacle. The obstacle clearance plane is based on a climb of 152 ft/nm, therefore, a climb of 200 ft/nm will clear an obstacle by 48 feet in the first mile, 96 feet in the second mile, etc. If no obstacle penetrates this hypothetical slope, no IFR departure procedure is published.

When an airport has both an IFR departure procedure and a SID, the IFR departure procedure will be incorporated in the SID. The same climb gradient of 200 ft/nm is required unless otherwise specified in the SID procedure.

To determine the required climb rate during departure, refer to the Gradient Rate Table in the front of both the Jeppesen and NOS volumes. Higher groundspeeds require higher rates of climb to guarantee obstacle clearance. For example, to accommodate a 200 ft/nm gradient at a groundspeed of 75 knots, you must climb at least 250 feet per minute; with a 100 knot groundspeed, a 300 fpm climb is needed.

It might not be possible to achieve these climb rates in some aircraft at maximum gross weight with a high density altitude. In these instances, you should lighten the load, use a more favorable runway, or even postpone the flight.

Occasionally, a SID climb gradient will be established to vertically separate aircraft arriving and departing different airports. Again, a minimum climb gradient will be published to achieve this vertical separation. Review the Gnats One Departure once again and notice that the required climb gradient is 400 ft/nm to an altitude of 4,100 feet.

After Gnats, it decreases to 200 ft/nm until reaching the appropriate altitude. A gradient rate table is provided at the top of the SID chart. For a groundspeed of 100 kts, a rate-of-climb of 667 fpm is required to avoid terrain and obstacles. If you cannot achieve this, refuse the clearance!!

An IFR departure procedure or SID may list ceiling and visibility minimums for takeoff. These minimums allow you to visually avoid obstacles. Strict adherence to these minimums is a must, otherwise, obstacle clearance is not guaranteed and you won't be able to see the obstacle in time to avoid it. Once you have crossed the designated fix at or above the specified altitude, standard obstacle clearance procedures apply.

If the departure airport does not have an instrument approach procedure, no obstacle avoidance procedures have been established and you are responsible for obstacle avoidance when departing. Use a sectional chart to locate the highest obstacles and terrain. Plan your departure route carefully. Any instrument pilot can be intimidated by the apparent complexity of SIDs and IFR departure procedures. SIDs can reduce workload, and IFR departure procedures are established for your safety. Study these procedures in the comfort of home or in the pilots' lounge...and then use them to your advantage.

Some SIDs are tricky, making you jump through hoops that don't seem to make sense. There's always a good reason for the required gyrations, however.

Many pilots don't take the time to really absorb what a SID requires of them before blasting off into the wild gray yonder. The one for San Jose is tailor-made for trapping pilots who aren't paying attention.

Case History: San Jose, CA SID

Not too many years ago, a SID—Standard Instrument Departure—was the kind of exotica reserved for Level 5 tracons. These days, just about any airport with radar services is likely to have a SID and if the airport has anything beyond minimal traffic, ATC will probably use the procedure regularly.

As we said above, SIDs simplify the clearance delivery procedures at busy airports and they organize traffic flow in patterns that work for ATC. They're convenient to the pilot only to the extent that they make clearances easier to copy and, theoretically at least, increase the airport's departure and arrival capacity.

The more benign SIDs point you directly on course; the annoying ones sometimes take you in the opposite direction before an on-course heading is issued. That's definitely the case with San Jose's Loupe Eight. There's just no other way that ATC can get north or northwest bound SJC departures past the inbound IFR traffic to San Francisco and Oakland.

SIDs aren't particularly difficult to interpret but we've noticed that one common error pilots make is to think of the SID as being two dimensional. They dutifully study the plate before departure, set up the panel for the route and double check the courses and radials only to blithely blow through an altitude restriction because they forget that SIDs are three dimensional.

Here's an example: Let's say we're enroute from San Jose to Portland, Ore. in a high-performance turbine. The clearance reads as follows: "November Eight One Nine Eight Victor is cleared to PDX, Loupe Eight Departure, Red Bluff transition, then as filed, maintain FL240, expect FL350 within 15 minutes, squawk 1234, departure is 121.3."

Your copilot hurriedly sets up the SID as ground control sends you to runway 30L. Your takeoff briefing is standard calls, the taxi and pre-takeoff checklists are completed and the tower answers your ready-for-departure request.

The after-takeoff and climb checklists are completed as you make the depicted right turn to a 120-degree heading. It's a beautiful day and you're sitting on top of the world. The plane's pretty light for this leg and the climb rate is exceeding 4000 FPM when departure gives you the other right turn and direct to the SJC VOR/DME. Passing through 13,000 feet while still southeast of SJC, the controller asks you about your altitude and whether you're flying the Loupe Eight. Your copilot replies that you're out of 13,000 for FL240 and that you are flying the SID. Both headsets are then blasted by an unhappy controller saying something about busting the altitude crossing restriction. Your copilot squirms and you both utter aviation's favorite phrase. And everybody else on the frequency is probably thinking the same thing.

What went wrong? Let's take a closer look at this SID, the clearance and the potential traps within. First, how many altitude crossing restrictions are depicted? If you said three, pat yourself on the back and take yesterday off. The first is the crossing of the SJC R-047 radial at or below 5000 feet and follows the initial right turn.

Since this SID takes you over the VOR twice, the next restriction is at that second station passage: cross at 12,000 feet. It's not at or below, but at 12,000 feet. The third restriction is to cross at or above 14,000 feet when crossing the SJC 8 DME fix northwest of the navaid. The VOR crossing at 12,000 and the restriction at 8 DME northwest are the restrictions most pilots miss, probably because they're fixating on the initial enroute altitude of FL240. The depicted "loop," combined with

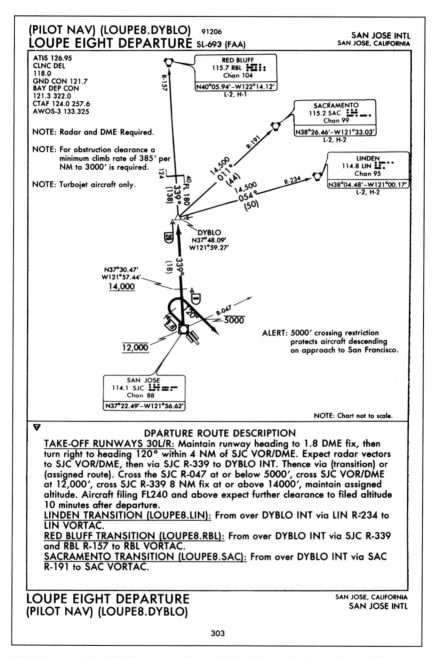

DEPARTURE ROUTE DESCRIPTION

TAKE-OFF RUNWAYS 30L/R: Maintain runway heading to 1.8 DME fix, then turn right to heading 120° within 4 NM of SJC VOR/DME. Expect radar vectors to SJC VOR/DME, then via SJC R-339 to DYBLO INT. Thence via (transition) or (assigned route). Cross the SJC R-047 at or below 5000', cross SJC VOR/DME at 12,000', cross SJC R-339 8 NM fix at or above 14000', maintain assigned altitude. Aircraft filing FL240 and above expect further clearance to filed altitude 10 minutes after departure.

LINDEN TRANSITION (LOUPE8.LIN): From over DYBLO INT via LIN R-234 to LIN VORTAC.

RED BLUFF TRANSITION (LOUPE8.RBL): From over DYBLO INT via SJC R-339 and RBL R-157 to RBL VORTAC.

SACRAMENTO TRANSITION (LOUPE8.SAC): From over DYBLO INT via SAC R-191 to SAC VORTAC.

LOUPE EIGHT DEPARTURE
(PILOT NAV) (LOUPE8.DYBLO)

SAN JOSE, CALIFORNIA
SAN JOSE INTL

303

The Loupe Eight SID has a number of altitude restrictions that a pilot must remain aware of as he leaves the vicinity. In an unusual bit of helpfulness, the reason for the restrictions is noted to the right of SJC.

ATC vectors and the lost communication procedure, makes for a SID that's more complex than most.

Nonetheless, as some instructors are fond of saying, it's all there in black and white if you'll just take the time to read it. Some pointers appear in the AIM and the FARs. One is in AIM paragraph 5-26(a)(2), which says that pilots operating from locations where SID procedures are published "may expect ATC clearances containing a SID." Bluntly rephrased, that means ATC may give you a SID whether you filed it or not.

If you accept it, you're expected to have at least the textual description of the procedure. If you don't want the SID, add "NO SID" (and/or "NO STAR") to the remarks field of your flight plan. While it used to be that you might not actually have the SID book, now that NOS is including SIDs in the approach plate books you really don't have that excuse any more. While it's legal, you're denying yourself important information about how IFR operations work at that airport and you'll require special handling from ATC. This slows down the works for you and for other pilots.

Without saying it in so many words, the FARs and the AIM define a SID as an ATC clearance and under FAR 91.123, it's assumed that if you accept one, you understand it and will comply. If you're confused, you're supposed to "...immediately request clarification from ATC." This provides some extra motivation (the rope?) to abide by the clearance.

In the scenario given here, you might argue that your flight was cleared to FL240. Nice try, but no banana. Take a closer look at the clearance. Notice that the altitude assignments are "maintain FL 240" and do not contain the phrase "climb and maintain." This implies adherence to the altitude crossing restrictions contained in the SID.

Since, in our example, we were given (and accepted) the Loupe Eight, ATC expects that the SID will be flown as published and the altitude restrictions complied with. The San Jose FSDO recently noted that the Loupe Eight altitude crossing restrictions are busted, on average, once a month.

We'd be less than candid if we said that we've never screwed up a SID. (In fact, we'd be lying.) But there is a way to avoid messing it up. Read the entire SID carefully before you go. Don't skim it quickly with one eye while taxiing to the runway.

This one (and others like it) are worth studying in the pilot lounge before departure. If we were caught by surprise and hadn't had a chance to look it over, we'd stay in the runup area until I was certain we had it down.

SIDs exist only because the airspace is complex and you are expected to perform accordingly. After all, is the saving of a few minutes to meet a schedule worth the trauma of a pilot violation?

The SID we just looked at is typical in that it really applies only to high-performance airplanes. For the rest of us, often SIDs and STARs simply are not applicable. That doesn't mean they're not useful, though.

These procedures are, in effect, a blueprint of the routings used in any given area. By studying them, a pilot can gain great insight into where he or she will be routed and why.

In fact, often ATC will issue part of a SID or STAR routing without referring to the procedure, itself; often this is because the procedure is for high-performance aircraft only. An example of this has happened to us: There's a routing in Connecticut that we always (and we mean always) get when approaching from the northeast, involving an intercept of a particular VOR radial. It's a pain to write it all down, but by this time we can rattle it off verbatim from memory. We were looking at the local STAR one day, and bingo—there it was.

SIDs Give the Big Picture

We're big on position awareness. Next to mastering a basic instrument scan, we think it's the most important skill an IFR pilot needs to develop. That's why we don't bore you with warmed over rehashes on sharpening your scan or drivel on partial-panel practice. We figure you can hold a heading and chew gum at the same time.

What do we mean, exactly, by position awareness? We mean developing the big flick; figuring out where you are and where everybody else is and using that knowledge to guess what's liable to happen next in the sometimes chaotic world of IFR flying. Understanding the local airspace is one of the key ingredients in position awareness. The more you know about it, the better off you are.

We think the best way to learn about airspace is to visit your local tracon and Center. But before doing that, do a little homework by looking over the relevant SIDs and STARs. In its effort to move air traffic safely and expeditiously, the FAA has become utterly regimented and largely predictable, at least around major terminals. The blueprint of that regimentation usually appears, in fragmented form, in the SIDs and STARs. If you know what to look for, you can use this information to your advantage.

SIDs are a growth industry in most parts of the country, as ATC

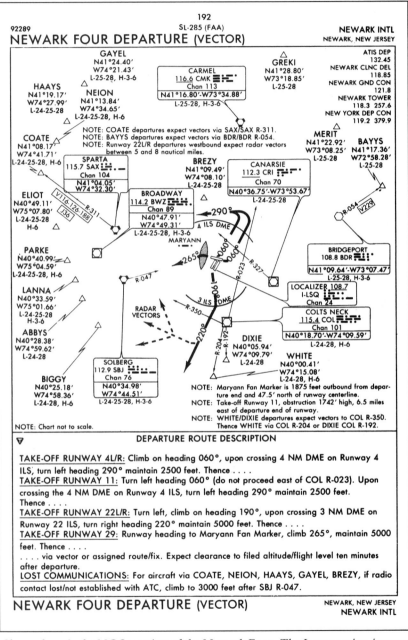

192
92289   SL-285 (FAA)   **NEWARK INTL**
NEWARK FOUR DEPARTURE (VECTOR)   NEWARK, NEW JERSEY

GAYEL   GREKI   ATIS DEP
N41°24.40'   N41°28.80'   132.45
W74°21.43'   CARMEL   W73°18.85'   NEWARK CLNC DEL
L-25-28, H-3-6   116.6 CMK   L-25-28   118.85
HAAYS   Chan 113   NEWARK GND CON
N41°19.17'   NEION N41°16.80'-W73°34.88'   121.8
W74°27.99'   N41°13.84' L-25-28, H-3-6   NEWARK TOWER
L-24-25-28   W74°34.65'   118.3 257.6
             L-24-25-28, H-6   NEW YORK DEP CON
COATE   MERIT   119.2 379.9
N41°08.17'   NOTE: COATE departures expect vectors via SAX/SAX R-311.   N41°22.92'   BAYYS
W74°41.71'   NOTE: BAYYS departures expect vectors via BDR/BDR R-054.   W73°08.25'   N41°17.36'
L-24-25-28, H-6 NOTE: Runway 22L/R departures westbound expect radar vectors L-25-28   W72°58.28'
        SPARTA   between 5 and 8 nautical miles.   L-25-28
        115.7 SAX   BREZY
        Chan 104   N41°09.49'   CANARSIE
        N41°04.05'   W74°08.10'   112.3 CRI
ELIOT   W74°32.30'   L-24-25-28   Chan 70
N40°49.11'   BROADWAY   N40°36.75'-W73°53.67'
W75°07.80'   114.2 BWZ   L-24-25-28
L-24-25-28   Chan 89
H-6   N40°47.91'   290°
                     W74°49.31'
                     L-24-25-28, H-3-6   ILS DME
PARKE   MARYANN   BRIDGEPORT
N40°40.99'   108.8 BDR
W75°04.59'   N41°09.64'-W73°07.47'
L-24-25-28, H-6   L-25-28, H-3-6
LANNA   LOCALIZER 108.7
N40°33.59'   I-LSQ
W75°01.66'   RADAR   Chan 24
L-24-25-28   VECTORS   3 ILS DME
H-3-6   COLTS NECK
ABBYS   115.4 COL
N40°28.38'   DIXIE   Chan 101
W74°59.62'   N40°05.94'   N40°18.70'-W74°09.59'
L-24-28   W74°09.79'   L-24-28, H-6
                     SOLBERG   L-24-28   WHITE
BIGGY   112.9 SBJ   N40°00.41'
N40°25.18'   Chan 76   W74°15.08'
W74°58.36'   N40°34.98'   L-24-28, H-6
L-24-28, H-6   W74°44.51'
                     L-24-25-28, H-3-6 NOTE: Maryann Fan Marker is 1875 feet outbound from depar-
                                        ture end and 47.5' north of runway centerline.
NOTE: Chart not to scale.   NOTE: Take-off Runway 11, obstruction 1742' high, 6.5 miles
                                        east of departure end of runway.
                                        NOTE: WHITE/DIXIE departures expect vectors to COL R-350.
                                        Thence WHITE via COL R-204 or DIXIE COL R-192.

DEPARTURE ROUTE DESCRIPTION

TAKE-OFF RUNWAY 4L/R: Climb on heading 060°, upon crossing 4 NM DME on Runway 4
ILS, turn left heading 290° maintain 2500 feet. Thence . . . .
TAKE-OFF RUNWAY 11: Turn left heading 060° (do not proceed east of COL R-023). Upon
crossing the 4 NM DME on Runway 4 ILS, turn left heading 290° maintain 2500 feet.
Thence . . . .
TAKE-OFF RUNWAY 22L/R: Turn left, climb on heading 190°, upon crossing 3 NM DME on
Runway 22 ILS, turn right heading 220° maintain 5000 feet. Thence . . . .
TAKE-OFF RUNWAY 29: Runway heading to Maryann Fan Marker, climb 265°, maintain 5000
feet. Thence . . . .
. . . . via vector or assigned route/fix. Expect clearance to filed altitude/flight level ten minutes
after departure.
LOST COMMUNICATIONS: For aircraft via COATE, NEION, HAAYS, GAYEL, BREZY, if radio
contact lost/not established with ATC, climb to 3000 feet after SBJ R-047.

NEWARK FOUR DEPARTURE (VECTOR)   NEWARK, NEW JERSEY
                                                         NEWARK INTL

*Shown here is the NOS version of the Newark Four. The Jepp version is more
than twice the size, and is easier to read as a result.*

attempts to fit more airplanes into a fixed space. Even relatively small airports have SIDs. The chief purpose of these procedures is to route traffic in predictable ways and to simplify clearance delivery procedures.

Here we'll examine the Newark Four Departure, a rather pedestrian SID but one that's commonly assigned to EWR departures. Wait a minute, you say, that SID is for jets and who goes into Newark anyway? True, not many of us fly into Newark but anyone who flies into any of the New York area airports—Teterboro, Westchester, Morristown, Caldwell, Danbury, Bridgeport and a few others—may very well be influenced by this SID, even though most will never fly it.

That's because New York's airspace, like that of other terminals, is defined by major arrival and departure fixes. Surprisingly, this particular SID is the only one Newark has; all the air carriers fly it in some form. Since it's the only show in town, the Newark Four depicts departure fixes with a clarity lacking on the en route charts. New York has what are called the west departure fixes, ELIOT, PARKE, LANNA and BIGGY and the north fixes, COATE, NEION, HAAYS and GAYEL. (Kennedy and La Guardia, by the way, use the same fixes so SIDs for those airports are very similar.)

Looking at the Newark Four, you can see that the general idea is to climb the air carriers and vector them to the departure fixes as soon as possible; up and out. If Newark is in south flow, using 22L/R, the heavies are up to 5000 feet very quickly and usually on their way to one of the departure fixes.

What does this mean to us flib drivers? For one thing, the flow patterns established by the Newark Four and New York's other SIDs dictate some pretty round-about preferred routes. For that reason, when weather permits, it's often more expedient to navigate through or around the New York Class B area VFR. In doing that, though, it's a good idea to be cognizant of air carrier flow into New York's major airports. With Newark in south flow, for example, and the jets well above, a VFR clearance through the south portion of the Class B area is a lot more likely than it is if they're landing north. Of course, time of day and the controller on duty influence the equation, too.

Second, the area west of Newark—Caldwell and Essex—won't have many departures so you can skirt the Class B area with minimum worries about jet traffic. (The arrivals enter on a right base and are well above the floor of the Class B airspace.)

When the wind is out of the north, though, skirting the Class B area to the west is not a good place to be. Note that the jets depart 4L/R and turn westbound at 2500 feet before climbing toward the departure fixes.

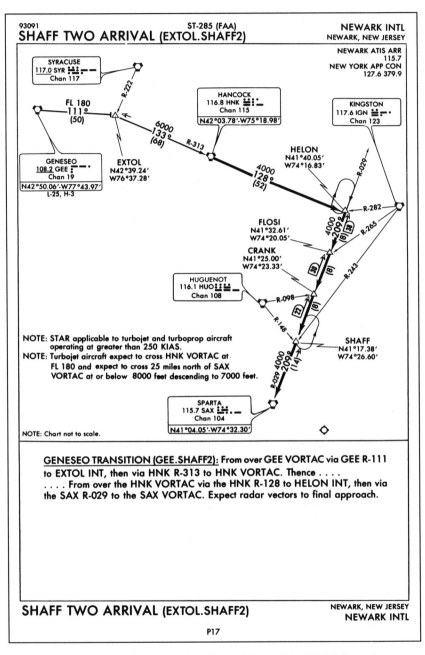

93091   ST-285 (FAA)   NEWARK INTL

SHAFF TWO ARRIVAL (EXTOL.SHAFF2)
NEWARK, NEW JERSEY

NEWARK ATIS ARR
115.7
NEW YORK APP CON
127.6 379.9

SYRACUSE
117.0 SYR
Chan 117

FL 180
–111°
(50)

HANCOCK
116.8 HNK
Chan 115
N42°03.78'·W75°18.98'

KINGSTON
117.6 IGN
Chan 123

R-222

6000
133°
(68)

R-313

GENESEO
108.2 GEE
Chan 19
N42°50.06'·W77°43.97'
L-25, H-3

EXTOL
N42°39.24'
W76°37.28'

HELON
N41°40.05'
W74°16.83'

R-029

4000
128°
(52)

R-282

R-029

FLOSI
N41°32.61'
W74°20.05'

4000
209°
(8)(38)

R-265

CRANK
N41°25.00'
W74°23.33'

(38)

(8)

R-243

HUGUENOT
116.1 HUO
Chan 108

R-098

(22)

(8)

R-148

SHAFF
N41°17.38'
W74°26.60'

R-029
4000
209°
(14)

NOTE: STAR applicable to turbojet and turboprop aircraft
operating at greater than 250 KIAS.
NOTE: Turbojet aircraft expect to cross HNK VORTAC at
FL 180 and expect to cross 25 miles north of SAX
VORTAC at or below 8000 feet descending to 7000 feet.

NOTE: Chart not to scale.

SPARTA
115.7 SAX
Chan 104
N41°04.05'·W74°32.30'

GENESEO TRANSITION (GEE.SHAFF2): From over GEE VORTAC via GEE R-111
to EXTOL INT, then via HNK R-313 to HNK VORTAC. Thence . . . .
. . . . From over the HNK VORTAC via the HNK R-128 to HELON INT, then via
the SAX R-029 to the SAX VORTAC. Expect radar vectors to final approach.

SHAFF TWO ARRIVAL (EXTOL.SHAFF2)
NEWARK, NEW JERSEY
NEWARK INTL

P17

Putting together the information found on a SID and the STAR for a given area will tell you where the heavy traffic will be. The Shaff Two STAR is the one that goes with the Newark Four departure.

They remain in the Class B area but you can bet there won't be any Class B clearances over the airports west of Newark, at least not above 4000 feet.

The traffic flow pattern established by the Newark Four and New York's other SIDs impacts GA traffic up and down the eastern seaboard, whether IFR or VFR. When filing IFR through the New York area, many pilots naively request V-123, which is a direct route that overtops La Guardia. Fat chance. Low-altitude piston traffic is shunted east on V-139, the notorious Shark Route or west over Solberg, Broadway and Sparta VORs. Just look at the Newark Four SID and you can see why. By the time the jets get near those VORs, they're well on their way to the flight levels, leaving plenty of room for GA slow pokes. That's why we say that it sometimes makes more sense to go VFR, with advisories.

High altitude traffic inbound from the west is also segregated from the jets, and fairly far out. If you're approaching the New York area at the flight levels in a slow turboprop or piston airplane (slow is relative here), expect to be assigned lower fairly far out, so the jets can whiz by overhead. Why? That's just the way it's done in the northeast; slow traffic goes one way, fast another.

The routing logic in the Newark Four—if you can call it logical—applies almost anywhere a major jet terminal squats fortress-like across your intended route of flight. To get some sense of how things work, study the SIDs and STARs side by side, visit the local ATC facilities, plug in and watch 'em work airplanes. Then, next time you're flying, plan to be where the air carriers aren't.

So far we've examined some of the more complex SIDs. The fact is, however, that most are very simple, along the lines of "Take off and fly in a straight line until we call you."

Even these simple procedures have their tricky side, however. The wise pilot won't be lulled by the lack of fancy maneuvering required to fly the departure.

SID Surprise

An instrument pilot once told us, quite proudly, "Oh, I never carry SIDs, because ATC always expects you to fly runway heading and you get a vector on course pretty quick." Honest.

Obviously, this pilot hasn't flown in the San Francisco Bay area or around New York, where half the airports have and use SIDs as standard practice. Or maybe he has flown those areas but just didn't pick up on the controllers' nuances: "Hey, Mooney 123, where in heck are you going?"

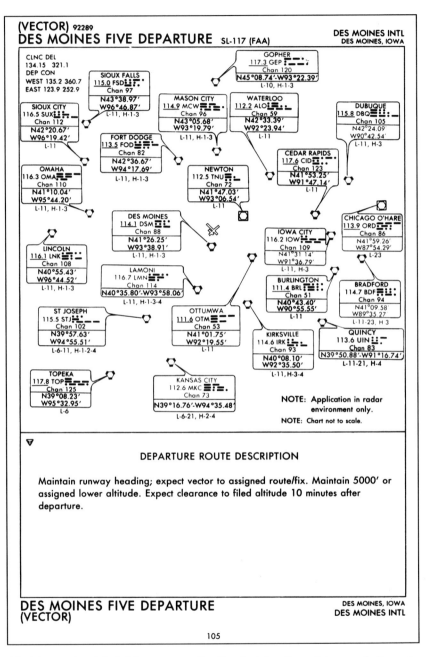

Nothing to it, right? Not necessarily. Be alert for the existence of alternate takeoff minimums or IFR departure procedures, indicated on an NOS chart by the T in a black triangle at the chart's lower left.

A quick look at the NOS North Central IAP booklet for Iowa, Minnesota and a couple of Dakotas might give some insight into this pilot's misconception. There are only two SIDs in the entire area and they're not much more complicated than "climb straight ahead; don't hit the cows." Minneapolis is the big city out this way and its SID, the Minneapolis Four, reads: "TAKE-OFF ALL RUNWAYS: Climb via specified heading for vectors to assigned route. Maintain 5000 feet or assigned lower altitude. Expect clearance to requested altitude/flight level 10 minutes after departure."

A few notes are tacked on for lower weather but this ain't exactly a tough SID, even though it's a busy chunk of airspace. The nearest big mountains to worry about are somewhere around Denver. Now, if we flip to Des Moines and the Des Moines Five Departure, we find similar directions: "Maintain runway heading; expect vector to assigned route/fix. Maintain 5000 feet or assigned lower altitude. Expect clearance to filed altitude 10 minutes after departure." This ought to be called the No-Brainer One Departure. It has everything except cleared for take-off and that's on the ATIS.

A redundant touch is added when clearance delivery reads, "...cleared to Devil's Lake airport via the Des Moines Five Departure..." ATC is then required to restate the altitude, "...maintain 5000 feet." So, you don't even have to read the SID yourself to fake your way out of DSM; open the throttle; close your eyes and ATC does the rest. (Just kidding.)

There actually are a couple of problems with the No-Brainer...er, the Des Moines Five. First, in the upper left hand corner (NOS version), note the frequencies. West is 135.2; East is 123.9. But west of what? Like most approach control facilities, those frequencies might shift geographical location depending on runway use configuration.

At DSM, the airspace is divided along extended centerlines from the active runway. "East Radar" owns half the scope and uses 123.9; "West Radar" rules the other half on 135.2. With runway 13/31 in use, just draw a line through the runway extended centerline, right across the scope, and East Radar is on the northeast side; West Radar on the other.

When they change to runway 5/23 (common in stormy weather), then the airspace is divided down the new runway extended centerline. How would you, as the departing pilot, know this? Ah...you wouldn't. If you didn't think to ask (most pilots don't), this bit of trivia would drop between the cracks and upon contacting departure, you'd be issued the correct frequency. If you've ever had this happen, airspace sectorization is probably the reason. Not every facility divides airspace this way and even when they do, things can change from day to day.

The point is, you should still be prepared for a different frequency than that which appears on your SID.

Also, note the "T" inside the black triangle down in the notes box. This means there's a telephone available on the field...no, that's not right...it means "Take-off minimums not standard and/or departure procedures are published. Refer to tabulation."

The tabulation is located at the front of the book and for Des Moines it gives takeoff minimums for runway 5 or 13R as 300-1. Runway 5 is the cross runway aimed at downtown and 13R is the "short parallel" (3202 feet) used by GA and once, by a confused DC-9 pilot. A followup note says, "Departure procedure: Rwy 5, climb runway heading to 1800 feet before turning left. Rwys 31L, 31R, climb runway heading to 1800 feet before turning northeast."

The reason for this is SkyView Restaurant, located atop the 40-story Principal Financial Building in downtown Des Moines. It's a members-only club; pilots and their aircraft are not welcome.

The DSM Five has a couple of other notes. One is the boilerplate, "Chart not to scale." Even though the VORs look close together, they're really not. Refer to the en route chart immediately after takeoff. The other note, "Application in radar environment only," is self-explanatory, or should be. The Des Moines Five is a radar SID. It even says "vector" above the procedure title. Vectors come from radar controllers and radar controllers need radar. When the radar fails or, as was the case last summer, the radar is being fixed or upgraded, the controller reverts to nonradar procedures and the SID is not issued. Without radar, you can expect a "cleared as filed; maintain 5000 feet, expect filed altitude 10 minutes after departure...."

Pilots don't understand non-radar ATC any better than controllers do so they often ask: "Is that via the Des Moines Five?" Answer: "No." In non-radar, expect to actually fly what you filed. Also, expect lots of delays.

As simple as the Des Moines Five Departure appears to be, it has one annoying side effect. Too many pilots interpret, "...expect vector to assigned route/fix..." to mean, "...expect *accurate* vectors to your destination." In the age of DUAT, loran and GPS, the FAA air traffic controller is still vectoring on a radar scope that would make Flash Gordon yawn. All controllers are required to have a pretty good idea of where neighboring navaids are as well as most airports within, say, 200 miles, plus a general idea of the location of the lower 48 states.

When a pilot files "Des Moines direct Minneapolis," they know that Minneapolis is roughly north, so the controller can tell the pilot on initial contact, "...radar contact, turn right/left heading 360, when able proceed direct MSP." They point the pilot in the general direction of his first fix and assume he/she can navigate "as filed."

Unfortunately, there are too many pilots filing direct to fixes off the edge of the earth, such as "Des Moines direct Wormgut, Georgia." Now, your garden-variety Des Moines controller knows that Georgia is roughly southeast of Des Moines, but they'll have no idea what a good heading is to anything so far off their radar scope. Best to have a plan in mind before you go flying direct anywhere.

Surprisingly, a number of pilots are asking controllers to do the navigating for them. If you file to a fix, we strongly suggest you have some navigation plan in mind that will get you to that fix without government assistance. Sure, a controller will help as much as possible, particularly if they've just vectored you 20 miles off course. But remember, you're the pilot. You know how to navigate, not the controller.

The Des Moines Five departure, like many easy SIDs, can be misleading if you don't do your planning. Finally, if you don't like the SID you're reading or your dog ate your booklet, just file NO SIDS/STARS. ATC will snort and grumble, but they'll read the SID to you and, possibly, whip up some abbreviated clearance that's easier to follow than what's published. Either that, or they'll tell you to stand by for a very, very long time.

Now let's look at the counterpart to the SID, the Standard Terminal Arrival Route, or STAR. Most of the things to watch out for when flying a SID apply here as well.

In many parts of the country STARs are not used much unless you fly something that whistles instead of putts. Still, you might encounter one from time to time even if you do burn avgas instead of kerosene.

Flying the STAR

Flying in a large metropolitan area can be intimidating if you are not accustomed to heavy traffic and constant radio chatter. The use of a standard terminal arrival route or STAR chart can add to the intimidation factor due to the complicated clearances and procedures listed. Reviewing the chart to determine which procedures apply to your aircraft before the flight reduces study time in the cockpit.

STARs are similar to standard instrument departures (SIDs) in that both procedures are used to simplify clearance delivery, and this is especially helpful when airborne. Without the STAR, for example, an aircraft arriving in the Dallas area on V-477 will be issued the following

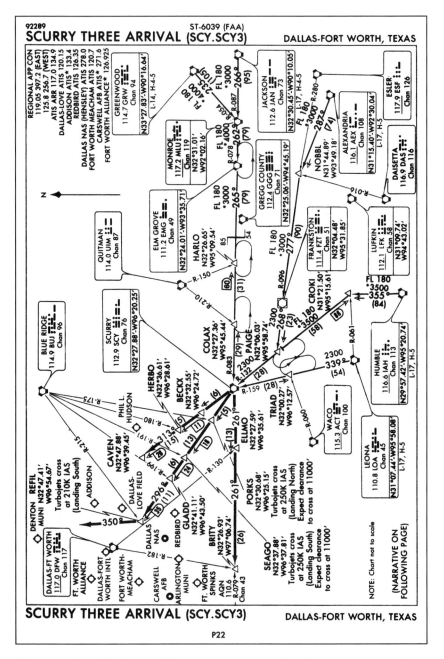

The front side of the Scurry Three arrival reveals a lot of complexity and chart clutter. Use of a highlighter along with study ahead of time can really help here.

92289
P23
ST-6039 (FAA)

SCURRY THREE ARRIVAL (SCY.SCY3) DALLAS-FORT WORTH, TEXAS

ARRIVAL DESCRIPTION

ALEXANDRIA TRANSITION (AEX.SCY3): From over AEX VORTAC via AEX R-287 and FZT R-096, then via FZT R-268 and SCY R-132 to SCY VORTAC. Thence . . . .

GREENWOOD TRANSITION (GRW.SCY3): From over GRW VORTAC via GRW R-235 and MLU R-054, then via MLU R-262 and EMG R-078, then via EMG R-265 and SCY R-083 to SCY VORTAC. Thence . . .

HUMBLE TRANSITION (IAH.SCY3): From over IAH VORTAC via IAH R-355 and SCY R-132 to PAIGE INT, then via SCY R-132 to SCY VORTAC. Thence . . . .

JACKSON TRANSITION (JAN. SCY3): From over JAN VORTAC via JAN R-266 and MLU R-087, then via MLU R-262 and EMG R-078, then via EMG R-265 and SCY R-083 to SCY VORTAC. Thence. . . .

LEONA TRANSITION (LOA.SCY3): From over LOA VORTAC via LOA R-339 and SCY R-159 to SCY VORTAC. Thence . . . .

TURBOJETS LANDINGS DALLAS-FT. WORTH INTL: (Landing South): From over SCY VORTAC via SCY R-296 to REFIL INT, then heading 350° for vector to final approach course. (Landing North): From over SCY VORTAC via SCY R-296 to REFIL INT. Expect vectors at SEAGO INT.

NON-TURBOJETS LANDING DALLAS-FT. WORTH INTL: (Landing South): From over SCY VORTAC via SCY R-313 to CAVEN INT. Expect vectors to final approach course. (Landing North): From over SCY VORTAC via SCY R-296 to REFIL INT. Expect vectors at SEAGO INT.

ALL AIRCRAFT LANDING DALLAS-LOVE FIELD, ADDISON, and PHIL L. HUDSON: (Landing South/North): From over SCY VORTAC via SCY R-313 to CAVEN INT. Expect vectors to final approach course.

ALL AIRCRAFT LANDING REDBIRD, DALLAS NAS, FORT WORTH MEACHAM, ALLIANCE, ARLINGTON, CARSWELL AFB, DENTON, and FORT WORTH SPINKS: (Landing South/North): From over SCY VORTAC via SCY R-261 to BRITY INT. Expect vectors to final approach course.

SCURRY THREE ARRIVAL (SCY.SCY3) DALLAS-FORT WORTH, TEXAS

The back of the Scurry Three arrival chart has the narrative version of the procedure. As with SIDs, Jeppesen users have a bit of an advantage with procedures as complex as this since the Jepp format permits larger pages.

clearance: "N54321 is cleared to the Addison Airport via V-477 Scurry. After Scurry, the Scurry 313 radial to Caven intersection. Depart Caven heading 350 for vectors to the final approach course." Whereas, a clearance utilizing a STAR will be: "N54321 is cleared to the Addison Airport via V-477 Scurry, Scurry Three Arrival. Depart Caven heading 350."

Preferred routes

Like a SID, a STAR is a short preferred route and is used while descending from the enroute structure to a point where you will receive vectors to the final approach course. They are usually integrated with the published preferred routes found in the front of Jeppesens or in the back of the U.S. Government Airport/Facility Directory. For example, the preferred route between Dallas and Houston is listed as "V-369 THY (Navasota)." From Navasota there are arrivals to most of the Houston airports. In the reverse direction, the published preferred route is "V-477 SCY (Scurry)." After Scurry, aircraft are usually assigned the Scurry Three Arrival. Flights between these two cities follow one-way airways and allow ATC to sequence arriving traffic well In advance of the terminal area.

Corner posts

The FAA has established "corner post" VORs in many terminal areas, and developed STARs for heavily travelled routes. Arriving in the Dallas area, traffic is directed to one of four corner post VORs. Each of these has an associated STAR. A look at the en route charts and the STARs for an area will tell you where the corner posts are; file to one of these VORs and expect the appropriate STAR.

Always attempt to file a route which does not conflict with the general traffic flow. This can be helpful when your destination is not the primary airport. For example, the Scurry Three Arrival serves 14 airports. Be familiar with the STARs even if your airport is not listed. You will know where the heaviest concentration of traffic exists. When planning a flight to a major terminal, one clue that STARs are used is the presence of intersections on the area charts. which do not appear to be part of any airway (the aforementioned Caven is one of these). The same is true of the intersections associated with the other corner post VORs.

How to file

To incorporate the STAR in your flight plan, file to the corner post VOR, adding the notation in parentheses under the name of the arrival. In this case, it will be "SCY.SCY3," the code ATC uses to enter the STAR in the computer and list it on a the flight strip. The entire route from Houston to Dallas might be listed on the flight plan as "V-477 SCY.SCY3."

Transitions

A STAR may incorporate a transition, which is an alternate route used for greater flight management flexibility. The transitions are depicted by thin lines, such as the one from Alexandria to Frankston to Scurry. To file this transition, you would list it as "AEX.SCY3." Transitions for flights of moderate length can often be used for the entire routing.

Occasionally, a transition appears that does not relate to any of the low altitude charts, such as the Alexandria transition. This transition is associated with the high altitude route structure. Notice that the minimum enroute altitude is 18,000 feet!

Speed restrictions

One feature of STARs which applies to the high altitude structure is that of speed restrictions. For example, at Porks intersection, there is a parenthetical note under the intersection name: "Turbojets cross at 250K IAS (Landing North)" This designates the point where a jet descending must have slowed to comply with the speed limit in FAR 91.117. This restriction is also listed in the textual description on the back of the chart.

You might hear a controller instruct a flight to "delete the speed restriction." This refers to the restriction at Refil intersection of 210 knots IAS for turbojets. A clearance to delete the speed restriction allows a pilot to remain at 250 knots for a longer period in order to save time and fuel. Pilots operating propeller-driven aircraft may be instructed to cross these intersections at or below a specific lower altitude to allow the faster descending jet to overtake them. Obviously, you don't want to be late getting down!

Profile descents

Another form of STAR which applies to turbojets is the profile descent. (Jeppesen users may occasionally come across one in their binder). This procedure allows a jet to descend without leveling at intermediate altitudes until reaching an "arrival gate" and continuing with a straight-in approach. The arrival gate is a point approximately one mile from the outer marker (or final approach fix for a nonprecision approach) from which the aircraft intercepts the glideslope and continues to descend to the runway. The profile descent was developed to help conserve fuel by keeping jets at altitude as long as possible before descending for an approach.

Lost comm procedures

Lost communication procedures when utilizing a STAR are not well documented. Since the objective of a STAR is to expedite arrivals, the procedures on the chart usually state: "expect vectors to the final approach course." In the event of radio failure, the route to be flown is dictated in FAR 91.185, which states, in pertinent part:

• "If being radar vectored, by the direct route from the point of radio failure to the fix, route or airway specified in the vector clearance;
• In the absence of an assigned route, by the route that ATC has advised maybe expected in a further clearance."

Without the aid of radar vectors, you could miss the localizer and not be certain of your position relative to the outer marker or final approach fix. In this case, follow the STAR to the last intersection and then proceed direct to the initial approach fix (IAF) and execute the full procedure. If already on a vector, go direct to the IAF and conduct the full approach. This procedure is not without risk, since controllers at high traffic airports have aircraft lined up ahead and behind you, and you will cut someone out eventually.

This is a real emergency when in IFR conditions, so you cannot wander aimlessly. You can avoid disrupting the traffic now by abbreviating the procedure turn with a holding pattern entry on the procedure turn side, or executing a 90/270 type procedure turn. Approach facilities are confident they will view your radar return even if you don't have a transponder. Once failing to respond to instructions, the controller will assume you have experienced radio failure and will take appropriate action. The only guidance for the pilot in these cases is that previously cited in FAR 91.185. Use your best judgment and land as soon as possible.

With the increased instrument flying and traffic at major hub airports, the STAR is a useful tool for ATC. Be familiar with these procedures and incorporate them in your flight planning so they don't become a surprise once in flight.

VFR Charts
in IFR Cockpits

M*any instrument pilots, once they get their ticket and answer the great Jepp vs. NOS question for themselves, chuck their old sectionals and terminal charts and never look back.*

But those charts are actually quite useful for the IFR pilot. Not only do they offer a bit of a safety blanket (as we'll see below), with the recent introduction of ICAO airspace designations there's now information you need that you can't get anywhere else.

First up is IFR contributor and Air Force fighter pilot J. Ross Russo, who relates his reasons for using sectionals when operating IFR.

Sectionals for IFR Flying

I guess it's true that we remember our failures more than our successes. I can still recall the questions I missed on my private pilot written, back in the days before the all-inclusive study guide had been invented. (Remember those blue Acme books?)

One of the questions asked what the FAA used as a principal means to get navigation information to the pilot. I don't remember how I answered that question but I do know I got it wrong. The correct answer was: The sectional chart.

The stigma of giving away an easy one has stayed with me because even to this day I make extensive use the sectional chart, especially when I'm in the weather and IFR at night. Curiously, most CFIIs tell their students to carry sectionals on IFR flights and to keep them open to monitor flight progress. But how many experienced pilots really do this? Not many, I'll bet. I find myself constantly justifying the practice to other pilots. They can't seem to understand why I like looking at "all that clutter" on the sectional.

The benefits of using the sectional are obvious to me. Compared to a sectional, a low-altitude IFR chart contains only enough information to navigate strictly by radio aids. In fact, you'll occasionally hear an old timer who came up during the radio-range era refer to an IFR chart as a "radio chart." Good as they are, the low-altitude IFR charts give the pilot only part of the position awareness picture. The rest has to come from visual details on the sectional and, if you're in IMC, your mind's eye. Pilots who don't use sectionals are denying themselves useful information about terrain, obstructions, airspace, and most important, the relative location of airfields that could provide a safe haven in an emergency.

Early in my Air Force training, I once flew an instrument cross-country from the back seat of a T-38. Although the rear canopy was covered with canvas, I was able to maintain a running commentary of my position relative to topographical features outside the airplane.

After the obligatory approaches had been flown at the destination, the examiner radioed for clearance back to base. He tossed a few questions at me during the oral but his final query was this: "How did you manage to give me a guided tour of this flight? I checked to see if you were cheating, but the canopy cover was closed tight. You got X-ray vision or what?"

Hardly. It's just that for instrument flying, the Air Force provides pilots with enroute charts, approach plates and SIDs. We got VFR charts but most pilots never bothered to use them on instrument flights. I was apparently the exception, at least in this examiner's experience. The fact is, if you combine your sectional and IFR chart reading process, you can just about develop the equivalent of X-ray vision. Because there's rarely a single chart that covers it all, this requires some effort and, depending on where you fly, a substantial chart library. I've found it worth the trouble and expense.

On some trips, it'll take a combination of an enroute chart, sectional, WAC, and VFR terminal chart. A good example of this is a flight from my home base in Panama City, Fla., to Tampa. As do most trips of any length, this route splits coverage between two sectionals; New Orleans and Jacksonville. There's just no way to piece the two sectionals together to get a good view of the route out of Panama City.

If I don't feel like messing with the sectionals, I'll use the WAC until I get in range of Tampa. Of course, the WAC's advantage is also its limitation; the larger scale omits ground and airspace detail, which is why I'm using it in the first place. Also, it's updated less frequently than the sectionals so the information is not as current.

I'll often informally merge visual charts with IFR charts. Since there's no terrain depicted on the IFR charts, there's plenty of blank space for notes on the altitudes and time limits of special use airspace or local frequencies I might want to use along the route. Sure beats looking that stuff up on the panels of the sectional.

As I approach the west coast of Florida, the sectional comes out again. I use VOR, DME, ADF, and loran to monitor my position. The loran's nearest airport feature is helpful in this regard. Florida has many more airports than it does navaids. I like to have sufficient position awareness to be able to put my fingertip on the map at any point during the flight and be able to cover my actual position.

Given the size of the average finger, that's a circular position error of about four miles; plenty good enough to deal with any problems that might arise. As I pass near or over an airport in VMC day or at night, I like to actually see it. This is much harder to do if you're navigating only with IFR charts, which don't depict the cultural relief and topographic features that are so useful in locating a small airport that's hard to see.

As I'm flying southward over the Gulf—whether day or night, VMC or IMC—I know that the first thing I'll do in the event of difficulty is to make an immediate turn toward land. I figure one minute of flying time equals a whole day's swimming and I'm not much of a swimmer. If I have to land somewhere in a hurry, on an airport near the coast or even on the beach, it won't do to transition from the IFR charts to the sectional while I'm trimming for best glide or troubleshooting an engine problem. I want instant, continuous position awareness so I can turn toward and identify a safe haven *right now*. As I approach Tampa, I like to know where I am relative to the Class B airspace. Yes, Class Bs are transparent to IFR aircraft but if I'm vectored out of or below it I want to know about it. VFR traffic tends to stack up outside and under the Class B boundaries and in those areas, I'll maintain an extra sharp outside scan. Also, I want to keep open the option of canceling and staying clear of the Class B area if it looks like heavy traffic will cause me delays. Canceling without the benefit of a VFR terminal chart is nothing more than an impromptu game of "you bet your wings," and the odds are definitely not in your favor.

One final technique for managing your cockpit: Try to fly with only two panels of your charts open, with the IFR chart folded and placed on top of the sectional. This will keep both the same size. They'll be easy to manipulate and much easier to read since everything will be in the same relative position. I use large stationery clips to hold the charts open.

Just as no one aircraft is perfect for all types of flying, no single chart is perfect for every trip. Real position awareness—that is, position awareness that will do some good when you really need it, comes from the ability to visualize yourself in relation to the features around you, whether you can see them or not. Besides, at $7, a sectional is one of the best bargains going.

Checking out the sectionals is now more important than ever, since the introduction of the so-called "alphabet airspace."

In the olden days, you could fly VFR with just your low-altitude IFR charts. Not anymore. Now, if you want to find out about the airspace you're flying through, the only thing that will tell you is a VFR chart.

Charts and the New Airspace

All things considered, the FAA did a great job of explaining the 1993 ICAO airspace changes and allowed enough lead time so that charts could be issued in time for even the most thickheaded pilots. The agency said the reclassification would be transparent to users and that's largely true. But there are some snags in the details. These relate mostly to how the new airspace is depicted on Jeppesen and NOS low-altitude en routes and on sectionals.

The upshot is this: in the olden days, you could fly VFR reasonably well using low-altitude IFR charts. Not any more. The airspace changes have effectively stripped the en routes of what minimal detail they had depicting the airspace around some airports. That kind of detail now appears *only* on sectionals.

Let's start with one basic premise. Class B and Class C airspace (old TCA and ARSA, respectively) are homogeneous, meaning that when these areas "exist," you won't find any other kind of airspace inside of them. In other words, gone are the days when a TCA had both a control zone and an airport traffic area inside of it. It's all one big lump now.

The word "exist" is in quotes because it means two things: (a) The airspace is officially charted and (b) it's within published operating hours. As far as we know, all Class B areas are 24-hours a day but some Class C areas may have posted operating hours. Outside those hours, the very same area may revert to either Class D or Class E. (Confused? It gets worse.)

The same rule applies to Class D; what used to be called a control zone. Class D is homogeneous and may have published operating hours, after which it reverts to Class E or Class G airspace. The operating hours are found in the Airport/Facility Directory and, on Jeppesen en

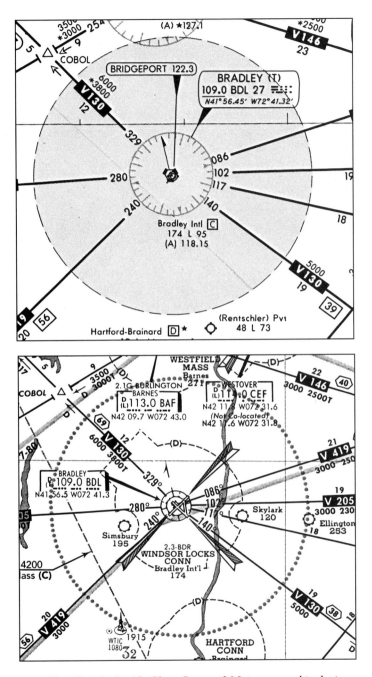

Does Class D exist inside Class C or not? Not supposed to, but some charts depict it. This should be corrected as new charts are issued.

routes, in a small note near the airport.

Having threaded the thicket thus far, you may think you're over the hump. All that's left is Class E (controlled airspace) and Class G, uncontrolled airspace and how hard could these be? Not very, until you start trying to identify them on the charts and discover that not all Class E airspace is the same. Back in the days when things were simple, Class E was called controlled airspace. On the newest NOS charts, it's shown as a white background area and it's basically everywhere, except in the Western states. In some of those areas, Class E is bounded by uncontrolled airspace (Class G.) It's shown on NOS charts as a brown shaded area and goes from the surface all the way to 18,000 feet MSL, where Class A starts.

Most of this is pointless, trivial detail but you're expected to know it anyway. You really *have* to know it if you ever have to talk a recalcitrant controller into a special VFR clearance in Class B, C, D or E-surface airspace. Used to be, all you had to worry about was control zones, but no more. Special VFR is now fair game in all those areas.

So, if you're going to fly VFR anywhere near airports of any kind, you'll need sectionals to know what kind of airspace you're dealing with. Class B and C are actually well marked on all charts so you don't need to sweat them, except when flying under overlying shelves.

But neither Jeppesen nor NOS depict towered airports surrounded by Class D airspace nor do either show the so-called E-surface airports, the ones that used to have a control zone but no tower. (Jeppesen area charts *do* depict Class D and E-surface airports, using segmented green circles.)

One thing to watch closely is airspace that changes its stripes with the time of day. Most Class D airports revert to Class E or Class G when the tower closes.

Because of an imperfect fit between the weather observer's hours and the tower hours, some Class D airports turn into Class E, then Class G after the tower closes. (We said the FAA did a good job of reclassification but we didn't say it was perfect.) Sectionals used to carry the control zone's effective hours in a small note but the new charts say "See NOTAMs/directory for CZ eff hr." Not only is that note less helpful than the old one, it's also a misnomer, since control zones no longer exist. In any case, check the A/FD for the hours and for those oddball airports that could be anything, depending on the time of day.

When overtopping Class D without talking to the tower, check the Class D ceiling carefully. We were told that most are 2500 AGL but in fact, we've seen many higher than that and some as high as 3000 feet. You don't have to talk with ATC to fly over a Class E-surface

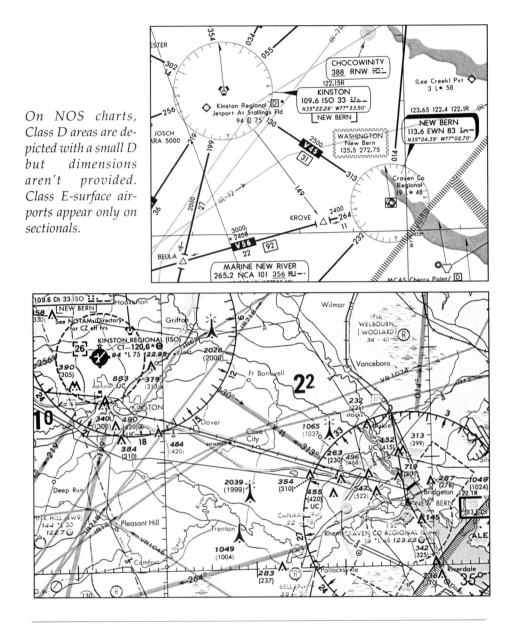

On NOS charts, Class D areas are depicted with a small D but dimensions aren't provided. Class E-surface airports appear only on sectionals.

airport...unless you're operating beneath a ceiling of less than 1000 feet or in visibility of less than three miles. In that case, you can exercise special VFR all the way to 10,000 MSL. Sectionals also show the diameter of Class D airspace. There's supposed to be a formula for determining Class D diameter—it's the point where the 40 to 1 obstacle plane intersects controlled airspace. However, the NOS charting folks say each FAA region seems to calculate the Class D diameter a little differently. In any case, expect Class D areas to be largest near airports in hilly terrain and smallest in the flatlands.

Some are perfect cylinders, others have arrival extensions. Some of those arrival extensions are depicted on sectionals in maroon rather than blue. That means they're Class E airspace, so there's no communication requirement unless you're operating special VFR.

Airport
Diagrams

Trying to find your way around a strange and busy airport after landing—especially at night or in foul weather—can be a daunting task. The bigger the airport, the busier, and the harder it is to navigate around.

Hence, it's vital to have a good airport diagram, and to be able to use it properly. Jeppesen and NOS both provide them, but there are significant differences. Here's an overview.

Finding Your Way on the Ground

Have you ever noticed how impatient some ground controllers are when an aircraft is stumbling around the airport trying to find the active runway? The reason is obvious: Controllers have a nice view of the taxiways from the tower but to a pilot on the ground, all those blue lights tend to merge into one confusing mass. Flying an approach to minimums on a rainy, turbulent day is child's play when compared to finding your way around a complex taxiway plan at night.

One solution is to always request progressive taxi instructions. But what if the tower is closed or ground is too busy to hold your hand or it's too foggy for the controller to see you? All of that happens from time to time, in which case your only salvation will be an accurate, up-to-date airport diagram.

Both Jeppesen and NOS publish diagrams. Jeppesen provides a detailed drawing for every airport, no matter how small. It's on the back of the lead plate. Major terminals are depicted on larger and even more detailed diagrams, many of which fold out to double the size of the standard sheet. The back of the double-size airport maps list

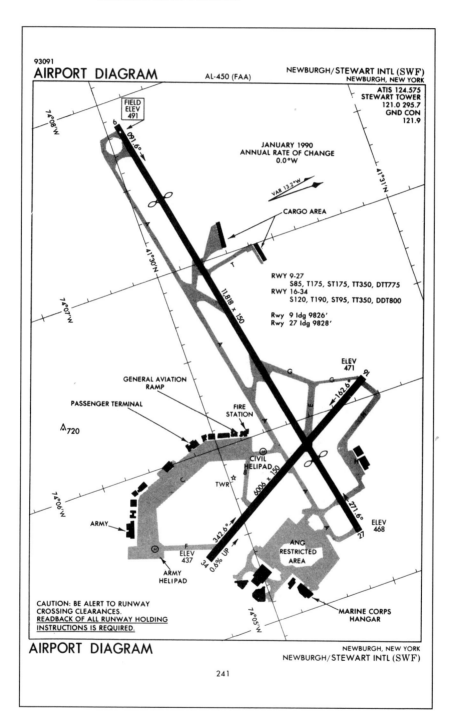

93091
AIRPORT DIAGRAM

AL-450 (FAA)

NEWBURGH/STEWART INTL (SWF)
NEWBURGH, NEW YORK

ATIS 124.575
STEWART TOWER
121.0 295.7
GND CON
121.9

FIELD
ELEV
491

JANUARY 1990
ANNUAL RATE OF CHANGE
0.0°W

VAR 13.2°W

CARGO AREA

RWY 9-27
S85, T175, ST175, TT350, DTT775
RWY 16-34
S120, T190, ST95, TT350, DDT800

Rwy 9 ldg 9826'
Rwy 27 ldg 9828'

ELEV
471

GENERAL AVIATION
RAMP

PASSENGER TERMINAL

FIRE
STATION

△720

CIVIL
HELIPAD

TWR

ARMY

ELEV
468

ELEV
437

ARMY
HELIPAD

ANG
RESTRICTED
AREA

CAUTION: BE ALERT TO RUNWAY
CROSSING CLEARANCES.
READBACK OF ALL RUNWAY HOLDING
INSTRUCTIONS IS REQUIRED.

MARINE CORPS
HANGAR

11,818 x 150

6006 x 150

AIRPORT DIAGRAM

NEWBURGH, NEW YORK
NEWBURGH/STEWART INTL (SWF)

241

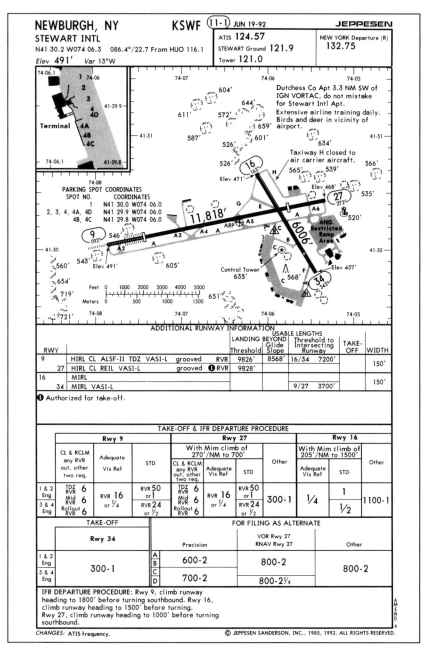

NEWBURGH, NY	KSWF (11-1) JUN 19-92	JEPPESEN
STEWART INTL	ATIS 124.57	NEW YORK Departure (R)
N41 30.2 W074 06.3 086.4°/22.7 From HUO 116.1	STEWART Ground 121.9	132.75
Elev 491' Var 13°W	Tower 121.0	

PARKING SPOT COORDINATES
SPOT NO.   COORDINATES
1   N41 30.0 W074 06.0
2, 3, 4, 4A, 4D   N41 29.9 W074 06.0
4B, 4C   N41 29.8 W074 06.0

Dutchess Co Apt 3.3 NM SW of IGN VORTAC, do not mistake for Stewart Intl Apt. Extensive airline training daily. Birds and deer in vicinity of airport.

Taxiway H closed to air carrier aircraft.

ADDITIONAL RUNWAY INFORMATION

RWY						USABLE LENGTHS LANDING BEYOND Threshold	Glide Slope	Threshold to Intersecting Runway	TAKE-OFF	WIDTH
9	HIRL CL ALSF-II TDZ VASI-L		grooved	RVR		9826'	8568'	16/34 7200'		150'
27	HIRL CL REIL VASI-L		grooved	❶RVR		9828'				
16	MIRL									150'
34	MIRL VASI-L							9/27 3700'		

❶ Authorized for take-off.

TAKE-OFF & IFR DEPARTURE PROCEDURE

		Rwy 9			Rwy 27				Rwy 16		
	CL & RCLM any RVR out, other two req.	Adequate Vis Ref	STD	With Mim climb of 270'/NM to 700'			Other	With Mim climb of 205'/NM to 1500'		Other
				CL & RCLM any RVR out, other two req.	Adequate Vis Ref	STD		Adequate Vis Ref	STD	
1 & 2 Eng	TDZ RVR 6	RVR 16 or 1/4	RVR50 or1	TDZ RVR 6	RVR 16 or 1/4	RVR50 or1	300-1	1/4	1	1100-1
3 & 4 Eng	Mid RVR 6 Rollout RVR 6		RVR 24 or 1/2	Mid RVR 6 Rollout RVR 6		RVR 24 or 1/2			1/2	

TAKE-OFF		FOR FILING AS ALTERNATE		
Rwy 34		Precision	VOR Rwy 27 RNAV Rwy 27	Other
		A B	600-2	800-2	800-2
1 & 2 Eng 3 & 4 Eng	300-1	C D	700-2	800-2¼	

IFR DEPARTURE PROCEDURE: Rwy 9, climb runway heading to 1800' before turning southbound. Rwy 16, climb runway heading to 1500' before turning. Rwy 27, climb runway heading to 1000' before turning southbound.

CHANGES: ATIS frequency.   © JEPPESEN SANDERSON, INC., 1985, 1992. ALL RIGHTS RESERVED.

Stewart is one of the airports that rates a full-page NOS taxiway diagram. There are some bits of information here that don't appear on the Jeppesen version, such as the location of the general aviation ramp. Both charts are slightly smaller than actual size, but are to scale relative to one another.

runway information and alternate minimums.

NOS, on the other hand, publishes what it calls an airport landing diagram, which appears in the lower right hand corner of every plate. While it has its advantages, it's really too small to show any appreciable detail.

Select airports—that is, those which have requested it and meet certain criteria published by the FAA—have a larger diagram that appears at the end of each airport section, just before the SIDs, if any exist.

We generally prefer the Jeppessn maps, for their clarity and attention to detail. But the NOS system has some advantages, too. One of them is that when a full-page diagram is provided, it's sometimes larger and easier to read than the Jeppesen version for an airport that doesn't rate a double-size ground map. Compare the detail on the two diagrams we've reproduced here, for Stewart International in Newburgh, New York. Stewart was once a major military airbase, hence the long main runway (in fact, in the days before good simulators, the airlines used to practice landings an touch-and goes there in airplanes as large as the 747). It's now an air carrier airport with passenger service, military operations and international freight service to Europe and Asia. (Last we heard, the Saudis were flying cattle to Riyadh).

There's a lot of information that's helpful to the pilot on a Jepp plate that a NOS plate doesn't have. Location of wind socks, tetrahedrons or wind tees, for example, along with a pretty good indication of how the surrounding terrain looks, using symbols for trees. Significant surrounding structures, like railroad yards, for example, can also sometimes be found.

When flying tnto the airport, a pilot using Jeppesen charts can pick off runway lighting, length and width, location of VASIs and PAPIs plus alternate minimums information, all from one sheet. NOS users have to hunt a little. The lighting information appears only on the landing diagrams (lower right of plate) and not on the detailed runway/taxiway chart. Once you've got the lighting code, you have to refer to the legend at the front of the book to learn that A5 is MALSR. Alternate minimums appear in yet another section of the booklet.

We have no idea why NOS doesn't organize the booklets more logically. Even die-hard NOS users complain about this feature.

Jeppesen subscribers get one bit of information that NOS doesn't publish: It's the amount of runway available beyond the glideslope, meaning that if you cross the threshold on the slope at the published value, you'll touch down with that much runway to go. It's intended primarily for jet operators but if you were landing a fast twin on a rainy day, it'd be nice to know what the landing and rollout margins are.

NOS's landing diagram does have another advantage over Jeppesen's version. The fact that it's placed on the front of the plate makes it much easier to refer to during the approach, should you need to know at a glance about some surface detail. Second, the relationship of the final approach course to the runway is depicted with an arrow and a line. This helps when you're trying to pick the runway out of the muck during a non-precision approach that doesn't align with the runway.

At departure time, once again, Jeppesen pilots have it a little easier. All of the required departure information appears on the Jeppesen diagram. NOS users have to look in yet another section for takeoff minimums and instrument departure procedures, if any exist. We also prefer Jeppesen's method of organizing the frequency box; it's easier to read with less chance of confusion.

For air carriers preparing to challenge the trackless blue oceans, Jepp publishes the lat/lon coordinates of the various parking spots, data that's essential for initializing inertial nav systems. You can calculate the same information using the grid on the NOS chart. (The annual rate of change in local variation is also given, for the purpose of accurately calculating position offsets.)

When using either of these chart systems, the best way to avoid getting hopelessly lost on the ground is to determine where you are *before you move the aircraft*. In the case of a departure, orient yourself relative to some obvious landmark, such as the tower, the terminal or a recognizable taxiway. Then hold the taxiway chart so it matches your direction of taxi and note the various intersections as you pass them. If you're anticipating these features on an unfamiliar airport, you'll be able to recognize them even if there are no signs.

At many airports, there are businesses on both sides of the field. It can be a long trundle to get where you're going if you turn the wrong way off the runway. It pays to know where on the airport your destination is (commercial airport guides like the JeppGuide or Flight Guide are handy for this). Usually the tower controller will tell you to "...turn left or right, contact ground..," or may even go so far as to ask where on the airport you're headed. If not, a quick request when acknowledging your landing clearance along the lines of "We'd like a right turn off the runway if possible," can save you a hassle after landing.

Just before landing, study the diagram to determine where you'll turn off the runway. Be prepared to tell the ground controller exactly where you've exited: "Twin Cessna Two Mike Bravo is clear of runway 9 at Alpha 3, taxi to the ramp." At a very busy airport, this will let the ground controller know exactly where you are. If you've anticipated the route, a clearance such as "Two Mike Bravo turn left at Alpha, right on Lima 3, then the outer to Charlie 3, right on Delta, hold short of runway 36, give way to the Citation taxiing our of Signature, ackhowledge hold short." will make perfect sense.

Chart-reading Traps

D ivining precisely what is meant by all of the arcane scribblings on a typical approach plate can be a fine art. There are many approaches out there that can catch the pilot who isn't paying strict attention unaware, simply because of some minor notation that's easy to miss.

But not all traps are subtle or insidious. Even the most straightforward approach plate can lead a pilot astray if he doesn't thimk—er, think.

First off, we'll take a look at an accident that, fortunately, killed no one, though it did destroy a very, very expensive airplane and leave one person with serious injuries. The root cause of the accident was not explicitly stated, but it appears to be related to a very simple and fundamental difference in the way Jeppesen and NOS charts their approaches.

The Mysteries of Chart Reading

Reading an aircraft accident report is often like reading a mystery novel: You know what happened, but you also want to know who-dunit and why. With the benefit of 20-20 hindsight, we often wish we could talk to the crew in order to find out why they went astray. This usually isn't possible, since the crew rarely survives a catastrophic accident.

In this accident, however, two fully qualified pilots flew a B-737 into the ground during an instrument approach and survived. Even though accident investigators were able to talk to the crew, they still could only guess what caused the captain to misinterpret the chart and descend too early during the approach. Follow along and see if you reach the same conclusions.

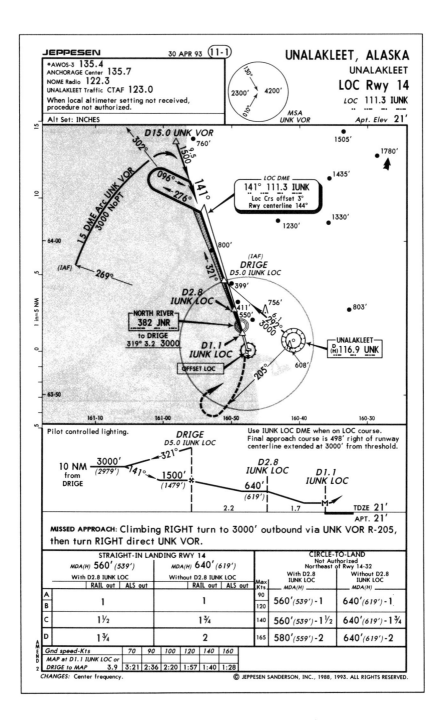

JEPPESEN   30 APR 93   (11-1)

UNALAKLEET, ALASKA
UNALAKLEET

LOC Rwy 14
LOC 111.3 IUNK

*AWOS-3 135.4
ANCHORAGE Center 135.7
NOME Radio 122.3
UNALAKLEET Traffic CTAF 123.0

When local altimeter setting not received, procedure not authorized.

Alt Set: INCHES

MSA
UNK VOR

Apt. Elev 21'

D15.0 UNK VOR
760'
1505'
1780'
302°
1500'
9.5
096°
276°
141°
64-00
15 DME Arc UNK VOR
3000 NoPT
269°
(IAF)
800'
321°
LOC DME
141° 111.3 IUNK
Loc Crs offset 3°
Rwy centerline 144°
1435'
1230'
1330'
(IAF)
DRIGE
D5.0 IUNK LOC
399'
756'
803'
D2.8
IUNK LOC
411'
550'
292° 61.
3000
NORTH RIVER
382 JNR
to DRIGE
319° 3.2 3000
D1.1
IUNK LOC
205°
608'
UNALAKLEET
D (H) 116.9 UNK
OFFSET LOC

Pilot controlled lighting.

DRIGE
D5.0 IUNK LOC

Use IUNK LOC DME when on LOC course.
Final approach course is 498' right of runway centerline extended at 3000' from threshold.

10 NM
from
DRIGE
3000'
(2979')
321°
141°
1500'
(1479')
640'
(619')

D2.8
IUNK LOC

D1.1
IUNK LOC

2.2
1.7
M
TDZE 21'
APT. 21'

MISSED APPROACH: Climbing RIGHT turn to 3000' outbound via UNK VOR R-205, then turn RIGHT direct UNK VOR.

	STRAIGHT-IN LANDING RWY 14						CIRCLE-TO-LAND Not Authorized Northeast of Rwy 14-32	
	MDA(H) 560' (539')		MDA(H) 640' (619')				With D2.8 IUNK LOC	Without D2.8 IUNK LOC
	With D2.8 IUNK LOC		Without D2.8 IUNK LOC		Max Kts		MDA(H)	MDA(H)
	RAIL out	ALS out	RAIL out	ALS out				
A	1		1		90 120		560'(539')-1	640'(619')-1
B								
C	1½		1¾		140		560'(539')-1½	640'(619')-1¾
D	1¾		2		165		580'(559')-2	640'(619')-2

Gnd speed-Kts	70	90	100	120	140	160
MAP at D1.1 IUNK LOC or						
DRIGE to MAP 3.9	3:21	2:36	2:20	1:57	1:40	1:28

CHANGES: Center frequency.

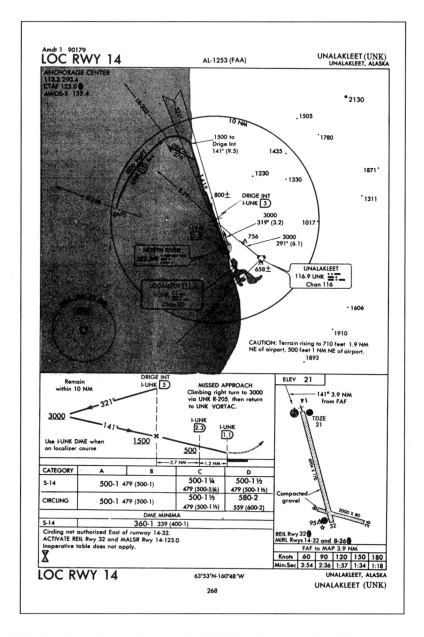

Note how the reference circle on the NOS chart is centered on Dirge intersection, while the circle on the Jepp chart is centered on the airport, itself. This may have contributed to confusion on the part of the pilot.

No pax flight

The airline flight departed Anchorage for Unalakleet, Alaska (about a one-hour flight). Since the flight was going to pick up passengers, only the crew was on board; captain, first officer and two flight attendants.

Forty-five minutes after takeoff, Anchorage Center cleared the flight to descend from Flight Level 310 to 8000 feet. The controller also gave them the Unalakleet weather, which was 500 overcast, 1-1/2 miles in fog, wind calm. This was barely above minimums, but was the first time in several days that conditions were good enough for a flight to get in.

The B-737 was equipped with a cockpit voice recorder, so we have the benefit of the crew's conversation. The captain started off right by briefing the first officer about the approach as they descended:

CAPT: Plan the Localizer 14, you got it out, via Unalakleet, which we're heading to the feeder fix, 291 [degrees], 6.1 miles, which takes us to Drige [the initial and final approach fix]. Drige, I'll just do a quick procedure turn headed back in, so I'm not going to straighten out on the thing, the localizer, just teardrop and come right back around and land.

FO: Okay.

CAPT: Three thousand till we're inbound. Drige at fifteen. Five at, ah, 2.3 mile fix, then down to 360, which is corresponding to 339 above. We got good enough vis. In the event we don't see it, climbing right turn to 3000, out the 205 and then we'll talk about, figure out what we're going to do after that once we get out there. [So far, so good.—Ed.]

Fifteen minutes later, the airplane crossed the UNK Vortac at 4500 feet and proceeded out the 291-degree radial to Drige. The captain crossed Drige and remained on a heading of 291° in order to fly a teardrop procedure turn to the localizer.

As the captain entered a right turn, the first officer said, "Going to 1500 inbound."

He was referring to the intermediate altitude of 1500 feet from the procedure turn inbound to Drige. The captain then made a confusing statement, "15 till 10 DME."

Apparently, the captain had in his mind that he could descend to 500 feet when within 10 DME, instead of 5 DME, shown on the profile view of the chart.

The first officer picked up on this confusion and responded, "You got the ten in right," meaning that the procedure turn had to be completed within 10 nm of Drige. Unfortunately, the first officer's comment was so subtle that the captain didn't respond and the first officer didn't comment further.

About one minute later, the first officer announced, "Localizer's alive," indicating that they were about to intercept the final approach course.

"1500 to 10, what we're shooting for," stated the captain as he intercepted the localizer inbound. Once again, the captain announced the wrong altitude and distance, which either wasn't detected or commented on by the first officer.

Indeed, the FO might have been confused as well, since he responded "Okay."

Moments later, "There comes the 10 to 1500; 500 feet is what we're headed for [3 second pause] 2.3 DME," said the captain. This was the third time the captain got it wrong. A conversation followed about preventing foreign object damage to the engines during landing, since the airport had gravel runways. The airplane was descending through 1500 feet at 9.5 DME.

Shortly thereafter, the first officer announced, "A thousand above the field, altimeters and instruments cross-checked, no flags."

The captain told the first officer to activate the runway lights on the unicom frequency. In a normal tone of voice, the first officer announced that he had ground contact. He obviously wasn't monitoring the approach or he wouldn't have been so calm about what was going to happen.

Two and a half seconds later, the airplane hit the upward slope of a 700-foot hill and traveled another 800 feet. Although the airplane was destroyed, only one of the flight attendants was seriously injured. The other three crewmembers escaped with minor injuries.

Investigation

During the investigation that followed, the National Transportation Safety Board focused on the approach briefing given by the captain, why the captain descended below the minimum altitudes on the approach chart and why the first officer didn't notice and try to correct the errors.

The captain didn't mention the location of the final approach fix during his briefing, which was Drige at 5 DME. Although he stated the proper altitude inbound to Drige (1500 feet), he later associated this altitude with 10 DME. The Safety Board believed that if the captain had announced the location of Drige during the briefing, any misunderstanding about its location could have been discussed by the two pilots.

Jeppesen charts were used by the pilots when flying for this airline. However, the captain was also in the Alaska Air National Guard and used NOS charts when flying C-130s. Therefore, NTSB reviewed the format of both the Jepp and NOS charts for Unalakleet.

The plan view of the Jepp chart shows an airport reference circle, which is a five statute mile ring around the airport and is intended to help you find the airport on the chart. On this procedure, the circle passes through Drige. The NOS chart, on the other hand, depicts a 10 nm ring that may or may not be based on the airport. In this case, the ring is *centered* on Drige. On NOS charts, everything within the ring is drawn to scale.

The Safety Board conjectured that the captain glanced at the plan view of the Jepp chart, saw that the ring passed through Drige, and assumed that Drige was at 10 DME instead of 5 DME.

But the captain could not explain why he believed he could descend to 500 feet at 10 DME instead of 5 DME. The procedure turn limitation on the profile view of the Jepp chart states, 10 NM from DRIGE. The captain conjectured that he looked at this note and connected 10 nm with Drige, since the D5.0 IUNK LOC listed below Drige was in smaller print. Neither the Safety Board nor the captain could decisively conclude the reason for the altitude/distance confusion.

First officer's role

NTSB then probed the first officer to determine why he didn't catch the error when the captain stated his intention to descend below 1500 feet at 10 DME. The captain was apparently amenable to having the first officer comment on his flying since, during the approach briefing, the captain remarked, "See anything you don't like or anything you question, just feel free to call it."

The first officer, who was experienced in reciprocating and turbo-prop airplanes, had only 80 hours in the B-737. His comment during the post-accident interview was, "I'm new in the airplane and busy all the time." The Safety Board concluded that he didn't monitor the approach closely since he was preoccupied with other duties.

Teardrop reversal

The Safety Board also reviewed the captain's decision to fly a teardrop course reversal instead of the standard 45/225 procedure turn. He was very familiar with the teardrop procedure as a result of his Air National Guard flying.

During the descent, the two pilots discussed the fact that another one of their company's B-737s was 15 minutes behind them. They wanted to get on the ground as soon as possible for a quick turnaround, since the ground crew would have difficulty handling two airplanes at once. The captain had an incentive to expedite the approach and a teardrop procedure would help.

The captain was legal to fly the teardrop turn according to the guidelines in the Airman's Information Manual. Paragraph 371 of the AIM states: "Headings are provided for course reversal using the 45 degree type procedure turn. However, the point at which the turn may be commenced and the type and rate of turn is left to the discretion of the pilot. Some of the options are the 45 degree procedure turn, the racetrack pattern, the teardrop procedure turn or the 80/260 course reversal." By flying the teardrop turn, The captain exercised an option allowed by the AIM.

In its report, NTSB concluded that the probable cause of this accident was deficiencies in flightcrew coordination, their failure to adequately prepare for and properly execute the UNK LOC Rwy 14 non-precision approach and their subsequent premature descent.

Your approach briefing

Although we still don't know what caused the captain to misinterpret the chart, there is an important lesson about preparing to fly an instrument approach, whether you fly a single-engine airplane or a turbojet. First, take time to study the approach chart at a safe altitude, not when you're preoccupied with maneuvering the airplane or talking to ATC.

Do you brief yourself before flying the approach by reading aloud the route, minimum altitudes and distances on the chart? Don't just stare at the chart, read the procedure aloud as if you were explaining it to someone else. Using this localizer approach as an example, you'd say, "After crossing the UNK Vortac, I'll track outbound on the 291-degree radial and descend to 3000 feet. When I cross Drige, which is the intersection of the 291-degree radial and the localizer, I'll turn right and track outbound on the localizer at 3000 feet. I will have reverse sensing on the localizer as I track outbound."

Continue talking yourself through the procedure. This will help you commit the important numbers to memory and reduce the chance of misunderstanding them. Keep the chart in front of you at all times, either on a lap board or yoke clip, for quick reference.

As you fly the approach, talk yourself through each step again if necessary to prompt yourself into further action. Use the five Ts (turn, time, twist, throttle, talk) whenever you cross a fix or complete a turn.

Two heads can be better

If another instrument pilot is along, do you brief that person on the approach and have him/her monitor your flying in case you get confused or forget something? Follow the same briefing procedure as before and explain to the other pilot how you will fly the approach. Make sure that person understands the minimum altitudes and distances for each segment of the approach. Also make it clear that you want him/her to say something if you appear to be deviating from a published course or heading.

Full attention required

Finally, don't let other people or factors pressure you into short-cutting the approach, e.g., passengers anxious to get on the ground, passengers waiting to be picked up, fatigue, etc. Your job is to fly the approach as published and make a safe landing. A low approach in IMC demands full attention.

Give yourself enough time to track outbound, lose altitude and complete the procedure turn in the distance allowed. Plan ahead for the airspeed you'll use and the time for tracking outbound. If you do it right, you'll have enough time to turn inbound and fly a nice, stabilized approach all the way down.

Make a missed approach if you feel rushed and uncertain about how it's going. The airport will still be there on the next pass.

Fortunately, accidents caused by misread plates are relatively rare. Still, plates are complex enough that lots of mistakes do happen.

We recently queried NASA's Aviation Safety Reporting System database to find out what kinds of things pilots get confused about when reading plates. The results were enlightening.

Plate Puzzlers

Suppose for a minute that you didn't know the first thing about instrument flying and had to devise some means for a pilot to descend through the clouds to a runway. Would you come up with the equivalent of a modern instrument approach and a plate to describe your scheme to pilots? If you didn't reinvent the approach plate exactly, you'd probably come up with something that looks a lot like one.

Still, using a thin piece of flat paper to depict a complex, three-dimensional procedure has definite limitations. Study any 10 plates closely and chances are, at least one or two will have some baffling details. On some plates, even the critical data is hard to understand, given the general clutter and chaos. As we just saw, those of us who rely on either Jeppesen or NOS regularly but occasionally use the other system are particularly at risk from errors caused by minor differences in graphic conventions.

Are these critical? They can be. At the very least, errors such as tuning an incorrect frequency or leveling at the wrong altitude might simply be embarrassing or cause for a separation bust. At worst, you could end up eating a dirt sandwich because you misread a critical value on a plate.

A handful of accidents have been attributed to misunderstanding or misinterpretations of approach plates and charts. It's impossible to say how many—if any—unexplained IFR accidents may have been related to mistaken plate reading. To get a feel for the potential, we asked the people at NASA to query the Aviation Safety Reporting System database for incidents involving confusion over a plate depiction or a procedure. This search yielded 178 incidents from more than 40,000 voluntary reports sent to NASA.

Accident picture

None of the NASA reports resulted in accidents, although without the limited immunity afforded by ASRS, some would have put the pilots into a serious jam with the FAA. Perhaps the most notorious plate-confusion accident occurred in 1974 and it did result in a horrific accident. A TWA 727 crashed into a hill while on approach to Dulles International. The crew had misinterpreted both the controller's approach clearance and minimum segment altitude for the approach. The NTSB responded by recommending that controllers issue specific altitude limitations when clearing pilots for the approach. To further clarify procedures, the FAA reminded pilots that course, altitude and distance information must be printed on transition or feeder routes and that minimum altitudes on those routes must be adhered to.

As we described above, confusion over plates may have been at least partially responsible for the 1990 crash of a 737 flying a localizer approach into Unalakleet, Alaska in relatively low IMC.

Errors of all sorts

Whether through skill, experience or just dumb luck, most of us do catch plate interpretation errors and those that slip by are usually of no consequence. According to the ASRS records, however, there's no lack of opportunity to screw up with plates aiding and abetting the crime.

Sorting through the ASRS reports, we found it almost impossible to categorize plate reading errors; each incident seems unique. In general, though, many of the errors relate to confusing typographical depictions, general chart clutter, puzzling notes, omissions and differences between NOS and Jeppesen plates. Occasionally, outright errors by the chart publishers are to blame.

An example of the latter occurred when two pilots were inbound to an airport in Arizona. The pilot flying was using NOS plates, his safety pilot was following along with Jeppesen plates. Both plates showed a different frequency for the CTAF and had they not heard another aircraft using one of the published frequencies, the two pilots had no way of knowing which channel was correct. We suspect that the NOS plate was erroneous or—more likely—a correction had been issued in the Notices to Airmen publication but the pilots simply missed it. A pilot inbound to Williamsport, Pennsylvania had a similar experience. He requested a NDB approach to that airport and was eventually cleared to fly it. When he had trouble tuning the NDB and asked the tower about it, he was informed that the approach had been notam'd out of service for nearly two years. In his report to ASRS, the pilot (an instructor), claimed to have current charts. He also said he had checked with FSS for the notam and was unable to find it.

We don't know for sure, but the notam was probably in the bi-weekly publication, which very few NOS users know about or bother to check. FSS may or may not will be willing to look up a published notam. The fact that pilots have to dig for basic information is a chronic failing of the NOS and notams system which the FAA has failed to improve much.

Another potentially serious problem with NOS plates that remains unresolved is that the booklets are occasionally missing entire pages or are issued with covers that don't match the contents. Again, these errors are announced in notams but the only way to be sure you've got the required plates is to look them up in the booklets before departure.

Jeppesen subscribers aren't immune to such shortcomings, either, but they're often pilot-induced. Over the course of a year, a Jepp user has to insert and/or remove hundreds of plates according to checklists provided by the publisher. It's very easy to overlook an insertion or forget to remove a plate that's been canceled. That very thing happened to one pilot we know; he showed up at an airport and requested to fly an approach that no longer existed. Not a fatal error, for sure, but embarrassing, nonetheless.

An ASRS reporter encountered a truly oddball version of the Let's Hide the Approach game. He was inbound to a California airport and requested a VOR approach. "The controller sarcastically replied that the NDB approach was in use...after frantic search, we confessed we did not have it." The pilot later learned that the NDB was an unpublished special approach, a fact the controller hadn't bothered to explain or perhaps didn't even know. The pilot retired gracefully and headed for another airport.

Variations in airport names and cities can induce confusion, too. Both Jeppesen and NOS index by city name not by airport name. Usually, the two names are the same but sometimes they are not and, in any case, there's no consistency with sectionals or en routes.

Let's say, for example, that you picked New Garden, Pennsylvania off the sectional and then went to look for it in your Jeppesen or NOS plates. You wouldn't find it in the Ns under New Garden but in the Ts for Toughkenaman, the town where the airport is located. From the chart alone, there's no way to know that. You'd have to work your way through the A/FD or an airport guide to sort things out.

Bad drawings

Considering the volume of data even a simple plate must contain, errors are inevitable. Tpyos...er...typos are a fact of life in publishing of any kind and can be eradicated completely only by throwing money at legions of proofreaders.

Even at that, a proofer may not detect transposed letters or misplaced numbers in a frequency box. To the untrained eye, none of this stuff makes any sense. Often, however, the data is correct, it's just that it's impossible to read because of clutter or ill-designed typography.

This can have unpleasant consequences for the pilot. On its SIDs, for example, Jeppesen, normally gives the departure frequency in the upper left hand corner of the plate. An older format, however, puts the freq in a large graphic smack dab in the center of the plate. If you're not used to looking for it there, it kind of fades into the background.

The poor graphic design of SIDs was cited by several ASRS reporters as a continuing source of confusion. One crew departing from Salt Lake on a SID mistakenly flew the lost communications version of the procedures, not the standard route. The controller caught it in time to avert a separation bust.

"This is the third time this has happened to me (different Captains and FOs)" wrote the pilot. "It has definite near-miss potential. It's easy to 'see' only the lost comm portion...of the procedure."

Another pilot reported that he turned to the wrong heading while departing on a SID because the procedure was particularly difficult to interpret. He had been interrupted while briefing and setting it up and had set the heading bug to an incorrect heading. Fatigue was a contributing factor, too; reading a plate when you're dead tired takes enormous concentration.

STARs drew some complaints, too. An airline crew inbound to Newark on the SLATE TWO arrival a few years back wandered off the published route and had to be herded back into line. The crew reported to ASRS that the STAR was poorly charted and even after discussing it in the cockpit for several minutes, they couldn't agree on how to set up the arrival. The reporting pilot said the STARs textual description didn't agree with the graphic depiction. Another crew complained about the very same STAR. It has since been revised.

Occasionally, a chart shortcoming is so bad or a procedure so confusing that everyone gets nicked. One of the ASRS reports described a poorly charted approach intersection at Pittsburgh's ILS 28R which, on a single day, caused five pilots to descend too early. In each case, tower controllers caught the errors. We weren't able to determine if this was an error or just poor depiction. Whatever the case, the current version of the chart appears to have been corrected.

Poor design

We've noticed that the way the charts are designed sometimes encourages minor, annoying errors. One of our complaints concerns the way frequencies are depicted on government charts. They're given in small type at the upper left or right hand corner of the plate, not consistently on the left, as Jeppesen does. Sometimes the freqs appear bold against a white background but if water is depicted on the plate, it's shown as a darker area. The overprinted frequencies tend to bleed into the dark background. The fact that the frequencies themselves are listed below the facility further confuses the issue. If you're used to Jeppesen plates, it's just as easy to associate the frequency with the facility listed below as it is above the numbers.

On some approaches, you'll have to look carefully at the NOS profile view to determine when and how a descent must be made. That's because NOS profiles depict stepdowns not as you actually fly them but as a continuous descent to the runway.

On several training flights, we've seen pilots confused enough by this convention to actually miss a stepdown or to descend below it. Jeppesen users are better off, in that stepdowns are charted with short level-off sections, just the way you fly them if you're doing things correctly.

The binding method—seven-ring binder versus bound booklet—causes its share of problems. Most pilots who've used Jeppesen have, at one or time or another, lost plates from the binder or dropped the binder while in the airplane. If it pops open, you've got a major mess on your hands. In IMC without an autopilot, this could be serious trouble. A few years ago, on a windy day at Logan, we saw a corporate pilot chasing his Jepps contents down the ramp after dropping the binder and having it split open.

NOS users, of course, have to engage in the epic struggle of holding the booklet open. One ASRS reporter discovered that this task is not without its hazards. On approach, he had opened the booklet, set up the approach and placed the open booklet on the right seat, with the approach he was flying on the bottom. Glancing sideways at the open booklet during the approach, he read from the top rather than the bottom plate and became disoriented before discovering the error. (As we noted in the first section, however, this will no longer be a problem by mid-year 1994, since NOS is abandoning the bound booklet in favor of looseleaf plates.)

Careful review

Some of the ASRS incidents were caused by flat-out errors but most were the result of confusing typographical conventions or complex IFR procedures that were poorly depicted. If you fly enough IFR, you're bound to encounter one. The best way to avoid them is to review the plate well ahead of having to fly it, either on the ground or en route.

Having a co-pilot aboard who can also brief the approach and monitor its progress is a real advantage. Just make sure you've briefed the right seater that his or her comments and suggestions are not an intrusion, but are welcome. Finally, develop a disciplined way of picking data off the plate. Any organized method has a better chance of detecting a plate error or miscue than does a hurried, haphazard review of the plate that changes a little each time an approach is flown.

Look...then look again. Whether you use Jeppesen or NOS, the approach plate's plan view usually tells you all you need to know to set up the approach. Sometimes, though, you have to look pretty hard to find it.

For this part of our chapter on chart traps we've collected a few real winners that can really flummox a pilot who's not scrutinizing the plate closely enough.

It's There...Now Find It

Government authorities use metal strips to band certain kinds of birds. The strips are inscribed with a notice to contact the Biological Survey in Washington but at one time, this was abbreviated: "Wash. Biol. Surv."

The strips were changed after a Vancouver farmer complained to the government. He wrote: "Dear Sirs: I shot one of your crows a few days ago and followed the instructions attached to it. I washed it, boiled it and served it. Worst thing I ever ate! You folks shouldn't be trying to fool people with things like this."

It seems that the government, even though unintentionally, is still fooling people, especially those of us using approach charts. we've collected some particularly baffling examples of approach chart puzzles here, some of which have to do with how the charts are drawn while others relate to how the approach itself was designed.

Hidden transitions

When shooting the ILS Rwy 29R approach into Stockton, you might be in for a surprise similar to what the Vancouver farmer experienced. Suppose you received a clearance for the approach while over the Manteca VOR. What's the correct procedure? Canceling IFR is not one of the options. There doesn't appear to be a terminal route from the VOR to the approach procedure track. At least there's no medium thick line with the arrow that typically indicates a flyable route.

You have to look *very* closely. Note that the criteria required for a terminal route (altitude, direction and distance) is listed underneath the

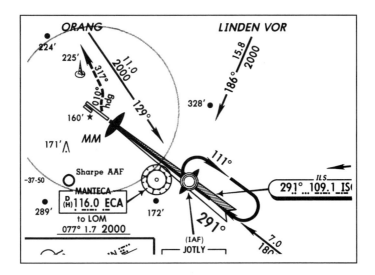

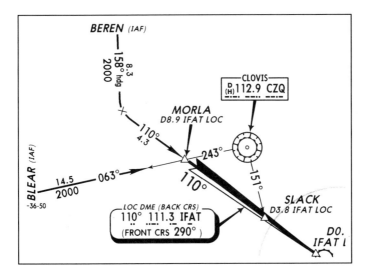

frequency box. On Jeppesen plates, when artistic clarity is important, routing information will be listed under the navaid in question. So if you can't find what you're looking for, check under the frequency box. Clearly, a medium thick line, drawn from the VOR to the LOM, would blend in with the localizer feather and you'd never see it. That said, NOS *does* chart the transition with a stubby little arrow. But because the feather isn't as bold on NOS charts as it on Jeppesen's, the transition is at least somewhat visible.

As we've said before, in addition to altitude, direction and distance, terminal routes always imply some means of positive course guidance to transition to the approach structure. Normally, this will be via VOR or NDB. Occasionally, no electronic means of navigation is available, however. Check out the Fresno LOC (BC) runway 11L approach at right. If you were at BEREN intersection and were cleared for the approach, you would fly a 158-degree heading as shown by the abbreviation "hdg" next to the route direction. This heading is flown until intercepting the localizer. For those of us who don't like doing anything with the word "Dead" in it, there's some comfort in knowing that dead reckoning routes are generally approved only for short distances (10 miles or less).

These routes are also limited to areas where, even with serious wind conditions, drift into higher terrain is unlikely. To hasten course interception, and further minimize the effects of wind drift, these routes intercept the inbound approach course at angles between 45 and 90 degrees. Curiously, NOS charts depict dead reckoning routes by default, without including "hdg." This is the government's delicate way of informing you that you had better have the DG set correctly and fly the heading shown until the localizer needle flickers to life.

DME arc confusion

Quite a few approaches have terminal routes that aren't identifiable on the approach chart plan view. At first, the Paso Robles VOR DME-B approach, left, appears rather benign. At least until you ask yourself why the DME arcs start at the beginning of the 077-degree and 179-degree radials of the Paso Robles VOR.

This is unusual, considering that the DME arcs meet all the criteria for flyability (altitude, direction and distance), yet the radials appar-

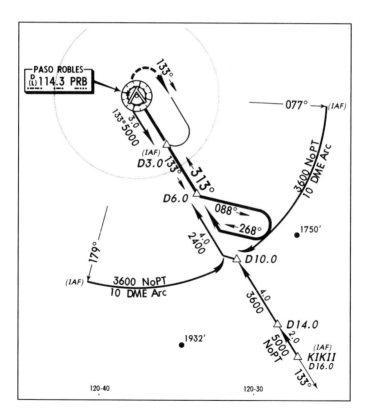

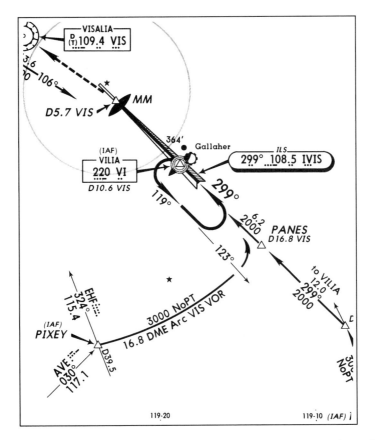

ently do not. These arcs appear to start in the middle of nowhere. The answer lies on the en route chart, which shows the R-179 and the R-077 to be V113 and V248 respectively. These airways are certainly flyable routes, yet they aren't listed that way on the approach chart.

Whenever a radial marks the beginning of a DME arc, that radial is *always* an airway. And airways are certainly flyable terminal routes. Many of us, when operating within the border of the approach chart plan view, crunch our en routes into little paper globes and offer them to the rear seat passengers as cockpit volleyball entertainment. Oops! Suddenly the mistake is obvious. Lesson: always have the en route chart available during the approach, just in case.

VFR airports

Jeppesen's plan view shows only those airports having IFR approaches. There's one exception to this rule. When a VFR-only airport is within 1 mile of either side of the approach procedure track (maximum thick line), it will be depicted. On the ILS 30 to Visalia, Gallaher airport is located just to the northeast of the Visalia LOM. It's a VFR airport but it's depicted anyway so you'll know it's there in the event of an emergency and/or so you won't mistake it for the primary airport.

Additionally, the five-point star located above the DME arc is a rotating beacon for Mefford, another VFR airport. These stars are helpful in identifying the location of any additional VFR airports. Unlike Jeppesen plates, NOS products don't show VFR airports in the plan view at all. Only the primary airport which supports the instrument approach is depicted. Again, when using NOS charts, it's important to have a low altitude en route chart or area chart (and/or a sectional) available, just in case you need to find one of these airports in a hurry.

Procedure turn secrets

There are times when pilots are expected to do certain things and times when they're definitely *not* expected to do something else. At Miami International, pilots signal the tower that they're being hijacked by taxiing to the end of the runway after landing with flaps down and engines running, without talking to anybody. The tower calls the police and they arrive to shoot out the airplane's tires. So what does a student pilot do when he lands at an airport? He taxis to the end of the runway, with flaps down and engine running, without talking to anybody. If the police show up and shoot out the tires, the student's enthusiasm for racking up further cross-country time is understandably dampened.

Learning the rules for procedure turns involves similar expectations. Approach plates are full of traps related to procedure turns. Consider, for example, the Ontario, Oregon NDB Rwy 32 approach. Since the letters "NoPT" are absent, all the routes on the plan view leading to the Ontario NDB require that a procedure turn be made. Your responsibility as an instrument pilot is to decide what direction to turn to intercept the outbound procedure course upon reaching the IAF.

There's no requirement that you turn in any specific direction to fly the procedural course outbound. However, common sense dictates that the aircraft turn toward the side on which the 45/180 reversal is made. Greater obstacle protection is offered on this side of the course reversal. Logically, while approaching from HOVEL and HOSTS intersections, you would turn right, intercept and track outbound on the 155-degree bearing from the station.

A right turn at the IAF, when approaching from these intersections, is the shortest way to get established outbound. When approaching from Boise VOR or PARMO and EMETT intersections, you can make

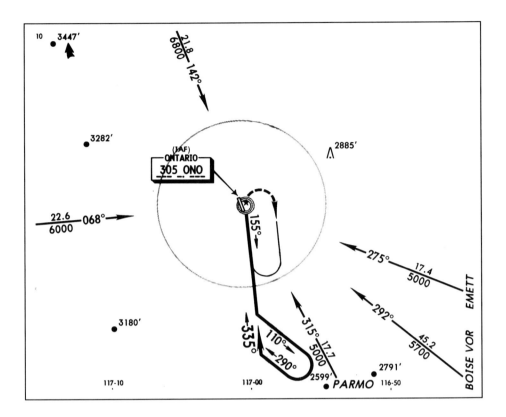

either a right or left turn to intercept the procedural course outbound. A right turn would keep the aircraft on the side that the 45/180 reversal is made. This side offers greater obstacle protection. However, turning left would be the quickest way to intercept the procedural course. Adequate obstacle protection is provided for either a right or left turn. Nevertheless, greater obstacle protection is always found on the turning side of the course reversal.

Race track roundabout

There are times when a holding pattern, used for course reversal, can create its own brand of confusion. The VOR-A approach to Corona, California, portrays only the holding pattern in the plan view. What's missing are the terminal routes. As an inquisitive instrument pilot, your first impulse should be to question how you can transition to the approach structure if there are no terminal routes depicted on the

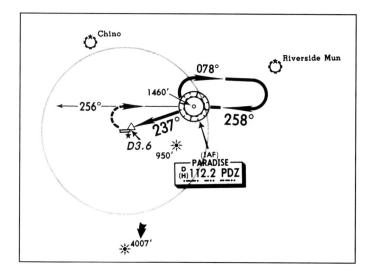

approach chart.

Radar vectoring is one way. However, in this instance, approach transitions are available but they aren't portrayed on the plan view. Once again the answer lies on the en route chart or the area chart. Low altitude airways are not shown on the approach chart plan view, yet they are an acceptable means of transitioning to the approach course.

The FAA doesn't require that airways be depicted on approach charts since they're already portrayed on en routes. Additionally, when an IAF is established on an approach chart, it's generally intended to be a fix that's common to the en route structure as well. This allows you to transition from the en route to the approach structure with less ambiguity.

Certainly, this is the case at the Paradise VOR. The VOR provides airway guidance and acts as the starting point for the course reversal. The en route chart shows eight separate airway segments converging on the Paradise VOR. It's likely that you may be on any one of them when being cleared for the VOR-A approach into Corona. Assume you are inbound from the northwest on V-197 and radar vectoring is not available. When you're a few miles from the VOR, ATC issues a clearance for the VOR-A. Are you required to execute the procedure turn (i.e. enter the holding pattern for course reversal), or can you turn inbound to Corona on the final approach segment?

There's no depiction on the airway or the approach chart which waives the procedure turn. The FAA's view is that the procedure turn is always required, unless "NoPT" is noted on the approach chart in the form of a NoPT arrival sector. Therefore, when approaching the Paradise VOR from any direction, either by airway or direct route, you are required to make an entry into the holding pattern for course reversal. Of course, if you were radar vectored, you're not expected to make the procedure turn unless you specifically request this from the controller.

The purpose of vectoring is to align the aircraft with the approach course. The rationale for requiring the holding pattern for course reversal is based on pilot workload. You may be approaching the VOR from any direction or altitude and while transitioning from the en route structure, you may need time to prepare. After all, you may be high and fast and could be caught with your wheel pants down. The course reversal allows your aircraft to be slowed and configured before flying the procedure.

When a holding pattern is used for course reversal, controllers expect you to make *only the entry* to establish yourself inbound on the approach course. You're not expected to make additional turns. If want extra turns in the holding pattern, obtain a clearance to do so. Additional turns may be necessary to lose excessive altitude or to allow more time to prepare for the approach. Making turns without permission could cause a traffic conflict, since it's possible that ATC—thinking the airspace if free- may clear someone else for the approach.

Nothing is worse than looking out the window and seeing yourself in tight formation with a 747. The only good thing is that you may get to watch the the inflight movie but then again, keep in mind this Confucian saying: "Pedestrian have the right of way, but rickshaw have more momentum."

While approach charts and plates have a lot of confusing information on them, sometimes (rarely) they're just plain wrong.

We've found so many errors on NOS plates that we're prompted to ask: Are they safe? The answer is yes, but only for pilots who truly understand how the government system works.

Charting Errors

We routinely compare NOS plates to Jeppesen products. This exercise has revealed a disturbing number of inconsistencies between the two and often, upon further investigation, we find that the NOS plate appears to be in error.

Most of the time, the errors are more annoying than substantive. There's the occasional misplaced leader or a typo that makes a runway designator incorrect. Twice in a six-month period, however, we've found NOS plates that have given lower-than-correct DHs or step-down altitudes, plus a handful of other depiction errors that could cause confusion.

If we've found this many errors in just a few dozen plates (a far from exhaustive survey) we have to wonder if NOS products are so shot-through with mistakes as to be unsafe in some circumstances. After all, on an approach, a pilot really has no way to double-check the plate. He or she is acting entirely on faith that the data is accurate and, in the case of an ILS to minimums, must rely on the plate's guidance to descend in cloud to within 200 feet of terra firma.

Is that faith justified when using NOS plates? We would say yes, but with this proviso: If you're not thoroughly familiar with the NOS system, including how it corrects errors and how notams dovetail into NOS products, that freshly-issued plate booklet in your flight bag may contain surprising errors. Most will be minor but some may be serious enough to occasionally compromise safety.

It may be tempting to blame these mistakes on government employ-ees more interested in the next coffee break than in producing an accurate plate but that's hardly the case. We've found NOS chartmakers to be as dedicated and as knowledgeable as their private sector counter-parts.

So where's the problem? It seems to lie in the way government plates—or at least the approaches themselves—find their way from the FAA to NOS and eventually to pilots. Although Jeppesen and NOS use the same basic methods to develop plates and both sources seem to catch errors about equally well, NOS's method of publishing critical corrections is far less effective than Jeppesen's.

Plates in a nutshell

To understand how errors are supposed to be corrected, it helps to know how plates come into being in the first place. Before a plate is published, someone has to invent the instrument procedure that it will describe. This is done by the five Flight Inspection Field Offices (FIFOs) across the U.S. As we explained in the earlier chapter on creating approaches, the FIFOs are staffed by pilots who are also well versed in the ways of TERPS, the government's basic approach design manual. Besides designing approaches, FIFO pilots also flight check them regularly.

Before an approach is designed (or, in some cases, revised) the need for it has to be established by the FAA regional office. The region works with local airport users and ATC, finds out who wants what then examines the airport and navaids to determine if an approach is even feasible. If it is, and there are no other conflicts, the region forwards its findings to the FIFO, which then gets on with designing the approach.

The FIFO specialists devise the approach (sometimes by way of a rough sketch used only by the FIFO pilots) flight check it and then send it on to the National Flight Data Center on a form called an 8260. At this point, except for the FIFO's sketch, the approach exists not as a graphic depiction but as a table of data describing the courses, radials, fixes and navaids upon which the approach is based.

The data center reviews the FIFO's work, checks the fixes, frequencies and other data for accuracy and makes the approach "official" by publishing it in the Federal Register. Every two weeks, a batch of approaches—new ones or revisions—are sent on to NOS in Rockville, Md., for charting. From the 8260 data table, a NOS compiler draws up the procedure as a draft, full-size on a piece of Mylar.

Checks and balances

Throughout this process, which consumes anywhere from three months to a couple of years, the data is continually double-checked for accuracy. At the FIFO, at least two specialists review it for compliance with TERPS. The flight data center further checks the FIFO's work for navigational accuracy, although without regard to how well it meets TERPS criteria. At NOS, the procedure is reviewed yet again, including a computer-based check of fix and course accuracy using a database supplemented by some sources independent of those used by the flight data center.

These reviews do weed out a lot of errors and they often provoke many phone calls between NOS, the data center and the FIFO. Nonetheless, even a simple plate contains hundreds of data points so mistakes do slip through the net, partially as a result of the diffuse, compartmentalized review.

Politics figures into the picture, too. Being a government agency, NOS is subject to pressure from congressmen who constituents clamor for fast action. This sometimes takes the form of a congressman's office phoning to ask for the hurry-up on a procedure. Review time is compressed and the probability of error increases. That appears to be what happened with the loran approaches that appeared a few years back. Not only do the plates contain errors, the FAA immediately notam'd them OTS because of ground equipment limitations. Obviously, the review has to end sometime and as the print deadlines loom a couple of weeks before the effective date of the plates, the review is frozen and the plates are approved for printing. If any errors remain, they will appear in the published plates.

However, as a last-ditch effort to detect errors, large or small, the plates are reviewed one more time, after they're printed but before they're released to users. Obviously, any errors found at this point can't be corrected in the booklets so FDC notams are issued describing the corrections.

It's at this point that the government's checks and balances some-times go awry. Serious errors—say an erroneous decision height or an incorrectly labeled procedure—are issued as p-notams (p for perma-nent) and will be corrected by issuing a revised plate at the next revision cycle.

Errors caused by temporary conditions expected to last less than 120 days (runway construction, short-term frequency reallocation etc.) are corrected with t-notams. Because the conditions are supposed to be short-term, the FAA used to direct NOS not to correct t-notam items with a new plate. The problem with this directive was that fairly important errors are sometimes corrected via t-notams and for reasons nobody seems able to explain, quite a few t-notams lived on for up to several years. This means that the errors reappeared in revision after revision, until either the t-notam was cancelled or was converted into a p-notam, charted and disposed of. As we discussed in the chapter on notams, that situation has now changed. NOS has the ability to issue interim plates to avoid this problem.

The notam system has always been the weak link in the NOS charting system. Everyone involved in producing approaches and plates admits it.

Anatomy of an error

As we said earlier, most plate errors are more nuisance than threat. Occasionally, however, there are serious oversights. One we found a few years ago concerned the LOC 2 approach at Keene, N.H. The NOS plate mistakenly depicted an immediate descent to the 1060-foot MDA after crossing the FAF. In fact—as Jeppesen correctly showed—there's supposed to be an intermediate step-down to 1680 feet before descend-ing to the MDA.

We reviewed the 8260 to find out where the error originated and it seems to have come from the FIFO. It was simply never caught during review, which isn't too surprising. The altitude value appears on the form in a box and unless you're a TERPS maven—flight data center and NOS reviewers aren't—it would be hard to notice. And remember, if a TERPS error does sneak by, the FIFO will catch it only after the plates are printed.

In this case, reviewers at Jeppesen appear to have caught the error and they drew it to the attention of the data center and the FIFO. The error was spotted just before the new plates were to be sent to reviewers.

Normally, a serious error—which this one probably is—would be p-notam'd and fixed during the next revision. Unfortunately, the mistake seems to have occurred as a result of airport construction. When the runway was resurfaced, the approach was temporarily converted from an ILS to a localizer, a process that's not as simple as it may seem.

Because the ILS was due to be reinstated, at which time a new plate would be issued, the step-down error was—you guessed it—t-notam'd, thus it was printed yet again in the next revision. (This was before the change in t-notam policy regarding the printing of interim plates.) Actually, the error was even reprinted in a Special Notice, a rare reissue of single, loose plates that NOS publishes to correct major amendment errors.

The t-notam first appeared as a Class I FDC notam. You'd have gotten it via DUAT or an FSS briefing. But once it was published in the twice-monthly Notices to Airmen, DUAT and FSS would have dropped it.

Could this mistake result in an accident? It's unlikely. But the existence of an obstacle just past the FAF did prompt the FIFO to call for the step down to meet TERPS standards. Because of the mischarting, the margin for error on the approach is greatly reduced and we would argue that when you're in the clouds descending toward the ground, you want all the margin you can get.

How Jeppesen does it

Obviously, Jeppesen did have the correct step-down for the equivalent revision so the question is, how come? Several reasons. Probably the most important is that Jeppesen does its own detailed chart review, quite independent of FIFO and NOS. And unlike NOS at the time, Jeppesen does chart t-notams that it considers to be of importance to pilots.

Moreover, Jeppesen plates are issued on a two-week cycle. It doesn't correspond exactly to the Notices to Airmen book publication dates but it's close enough so that subscribers get a steady trickle of new plates reflecting the latest changes. If a t-notam changes a DH or MDA or whatever, Jeppesen simply reissues a new plate showing the change. When, for whatever reason, Jeppesen isn't able to chart the change, it does include notice of it in the regular chart notams it sends subscribers.

In any case, Jeppesen subscribers get something every two weeks, either revised charts or notams announcing changes. Any revisions that fall between the cracks (which aren't many) should be available through DUAT or FSS.

Jeppesen's plate production process is also under one roof and this appears to be more efficient, resulting in more review time and fewer errors. As does NOS, Jeppesen gets the raw 8260 from the flight data center and compiles its plates from the same information the government uses. However, Jeppesen has on-staff reviewers who are well-versed in TERPS. If anything seems amiss, they'll contact the flight data center or the appropriate FIFO for clarification.

As happened with the Keene localizer approach, Jeppesen reviewers often flag errors the others may have missed and the corrections will be passed on to NOS through the data center.

Jeppesen prepares plates on CAD equipment tied into a navigation database, rather than by hand, as does NOS. This improves accuracy too since fixes and courses are checked as they're drawn, not after the fact. The CAD system won't, however, detect errors in the minimums boxes, missed approach segments or in special notes. That still requires a human touch.

As a further hedge against errors, Jeppesen has constructed its own navigation database, using both data from the flight data center and from its own independent sources. Furthermore, on a daily basis, Jeppesen keeps track of every notam the government issues, with an eye toward charting significant changes as soon as possible.

All this is not to say Jeppesen is perfect. They make mistakes, too and sometimes NOS or the FIFOs discover the error and pass the word back to Jeppesen. However, because of the two-week revision cycle, Jeppesen has more than 24 opportunities each year to correct its errors so in general, they're shorter lived if not less obvious. Also, Jeppesen subscribers are force-fed corrections, since the company's products are available only by subscription.

What it all means

At the outset, we said that NOS plates aren't so error prone as to be unsafe, *providing you understand the system*. This caveat has to be stated in the strongest terms. Unfortunately, as the people at NOS are quick to admit, very few pilots really do understand how the system works, especially those who buy booklets piecemeal, rather than subscribing. But even subscribers are often confused. One NOS plate reviewer told us that at Oshkosh that a subscriber explained how pleased he was with the NOS chart service. But he wondered why the government couldn't save itself some money by sending all of the booklets in the same box.

Every two months, it seemed, a separate booklet arrived late.

The pilot was referring, of course, to the off-cycle Change Notice, in which NOS announces revisions, additions and deletions to the previous volumes. Evidently, the pilot had no idea of what the Change Notice was or how to use it. Pilots who buy NOS plates off the shelf generally aren't confused by the Change Notice, though. Many have never heard of it.

Worse yet is the notams dilemma. The twice-monthly Notices to Airman is available from the Government Printing Office by subscription. For all practical purposes, you really have to consider it as part of a subscription to NOS plates.

But hardly anyone subscribes to notams, a situation that both the FAA and NOS are acutely aware of. The NOS print run for plates is about 300,000 per cycle, of which about 15,000 are subscribers. We couldn't determine how many NOS subscribers also take notams but we suspect that the number is quite small.

Conclusion

You can count on the fingers of one hand the accidents that have occurred because of gross charting errors. You'd need your fingers and toes to tally up the ones that were, in some way, the result of approach plate confusion. The point is, NOS plates aren't littered with phoney data just waiting to lure you into premature contact with Mother Earth.

But, next time you're whizzing down to MDA on a localizer, ask yourself if it's important to be sure what MDA *really* is. If you don't mind giving away a few hundred feet of obstacle protection or having the wrong frequency or wrong course from time to time, don't sweat it. You'll probably be okay.

On the other hand, if you really want the best data the government can provide, get cozy with the NOS update system and subscribe to and regularly check the printed notams.

Reading the Fine Print

O ur purpose with this chapter is to lend insight into the fine art of chart reading, taking a close look at the details rather than presenting a treatise on the basics. We'll be covering a broad spectrum here, from frequency boxes on en routes to minimum equipment notes on approach plates.

First up is a brief look at the "bad" old days: we recently unearthed an approach plate circa 1969, and compared it with the same approach plate in use today. Times have certainly changed...for the better, mostly, but there are some features on the old chart that we like. See what you think.

Something Old, Something New

We recently came across an old VOR approach chart for Martinsburg WV, circa 1969. Reviewing this old chart was interesting in that many of the current "problems" with the NOS approach plate books aren't found on it. For example, where current charts (in the name of decluttering) have buried much of the important information such as lighting systems and instrument departure procedures elsewhere in the book, the older format puts them on the plate, itself.

Notice the instrument departure procedure is printed on the plan view: "For West departure on V8, V44, V166 from Runway 26..." Now there's an interesting idea. You don't need to hunt in an index somewhere to find out if a departure procedure is available; just look at the chart. We realize, of course, this isn't practical since multiple departure procedures would only clutter the chart. But it is tempting, and after all, Jeppesen manages to do it....

Compare this with the current procedure on the right and you'll see

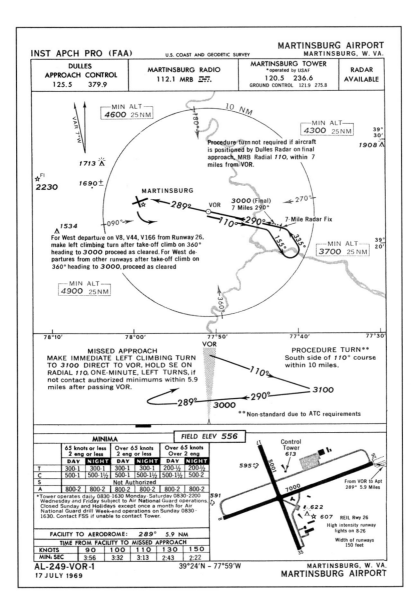

MARTINSBURG AIRPORT
MARTINSBURG, W. VA.

INST APCH PRO (FAA)   U.S. COAST AND GEODETIC SURVEY

| DULLES APPROACH CONTROL 125.5 379.9 | MARTINSBURG RADIO 112.1 MRB | MARTINSBURG TOWER *operated by USAF 120.5 236.6 GROUND CONTROL 121.9 275.8 | RADAR AVAILABLE |

MIN ALT 4600 25NM

10 NM

MIN ALT 4300 25NM

39° 30'
1908

Procedure turn not required if aircraft is positioned by Dulles Radar on final approach, MRB Radial 110, within 7 miles from VOR.

1713

FI 2230   1690±

MARTINSBURG

289°   VOR   3000 (Final) 7 Miles 290°   270°

090°   290°   7-Mile Radar Fix

110°   335°   155°

1534

For West departure on V8, V44, V166 from Runway 26, make left climbing turn after take-off climb on 360° heading to 3000 proceed as cleared. For West departures from other runways after take-off climb on 360° heading to 3000, proceed as cleared

MIN ALT 3700 25NM   39° 20'

MIN ALT 4900 25NM   360°

78°10'   78°00'   77°50' VOR   77°40'   77°30'

MISSED APPROACH
MAKE IMMEDIATE LEFT CLIMBING TURN TO 3100 DIRECT TO VOR, HOLD SE ON RADIAL 110, ONE-MINUTE, LEFT TURNS, if not contact authorized minimums within 5.9 miles after passing VOR.

110°

PROCEDURE TURN
South side of 110° course within 10 miles.

3100

289°   3000   290°

** Non-standard due to ATC requirements

MINIMA

FIELD ELEV 556

	65 knots or less 2 eng or less		Over 65 knots 2 eng or less		Over 65 knots Over 2 eng	
	DAY	NIGHT	DAY	NIGHT	DAY	NIGHT
T	300-1	300-1	300-1	300-1	200-½	200-½
C	500-1	500-1½	500-1	500-1½	500-1½	500-2
S			Not Authorized			
A	800-2	800-2	800-2	800-2	800-2	800-2

*Tower operates daily 0830-1630 Monday-Saturday 0830-2200 Wednesday and Friday subject to Air National Guard operations. Closed Sunday and Holidays except once a month for Air National Guard drill Week-end operations on Sunday 0830-1630. Contact FSS if unable to contact Tower.

Control Tower 613

595

5000   7000

From VOR to Apt 289° 5.9 Miles

591   622

607   REIL Rwy 26

High intensity runway lights on 8-26

Width of runways 150 feet

FACILITY TO AERODROME:	289°	5.9 NM		
TIME FROM FACILITY TO MISSED APPROACH				
KNOTS	90	100	110	130	150
MIN: SEC	3:56	3:32	3:13	2:43	2:22

AL-249-VOR-1
17 JULY 1969

39°24'N – 77°59'W

MARTINSBURG, W. VA.
MARTINSBURG AIRPORT

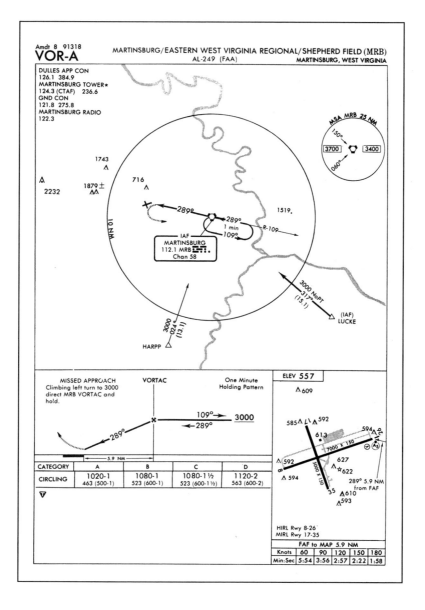

Amdt 8 91318

VOR-A

MARTINSBURG/EASTERN WEST VIRGINIA REGIONAL/SHEPHERD FIELD (MRB)
AL-249 (FAA)

MARTINSBURG, WEST VIRGINIA

DULLES APP CON
126.1 384.9
MARTINSBURG TOWER★
124.3 (CTAF) 236.6
GND CON
121.8 275.8
MARTINSBURG RADIO
122.3

MSA MRB 25 NM

150° 3700 ◈ 3400 060°

1743

2232

1879 ±

716

1519.

289°

289°
1 min
109°

R-109

IAF
MARTINSBURG
112.1 MRB ▪▪▪
Chan 58

3000 NoPT
317°
(15.1)

(IAF)
LUCKE

3000
024
(13.1)

HARPP

10 NM

MISSED APPROACH
Climbing left turn to 3000
direct MRB VORTAC and
hold.

VORTAC

One Minute
Holding Pattern

ELEV 557

609

109° → 3000
← 289°

289°

5.9 NM

585 592

613
7000 X 150

594

592

627

622

594

289° 5.9 NM
from FAF

35

610

593

CATEGORY	A	B	C	D
CIRCLING	1020-1 463 (500-1)	1080-1 523 (600-1)	1080-1½ 523 (600-1½)	1120-2 563 (600-2)

HIRL Rwy 8-26
MIRL Rwy 17-35

FAF to MAP 5.9 NM					
Knots	60	90	120	150	180
Min:Sec	5:54	3:56	2:57	2:22	1:58

how much clutter has been reduced through the years. The minimums section was also listed differently. The MDA shown on the old chart is agl, which means you had to add the MDA to the field elevation, instead of the current MDA in msl. The T, C, S, A on the left side are minimums for takeoff, circling, straight-in and alternate. Once again, no need to look up takeoff and alternate minimums.

On the profile view, we must confess the larger print for the missed approach instructions on the old chart is easier to read. Maybe we should just get bifocals instead. You need to look on the top of the old chart for the VOR frequency. It's easier to locate on the current one.

As we noted earlier in the book, given the task of preparing instructions for landing in instrument conditions and placing them on a small piece of paper is likely to result in something very much like, if not identical to, an approach plate.

Still, there are many ways to present the information. Like anything else in aviation, how the plate is designed is a compromise, in this case between the amount of information presented and the chart clutter it creates. Clearly, the trend in recent years has been away from clutter at the expense of cryptic symbology and codes.

Because of the complex nature of some approach plates, we recommend that a pilot always get familiar with the approaches for his or her destination even before the airplane is preflighted.

That doesn't mean it's necessary to memorize everything about all of the approaches an airport has; rather, it's a good idea to look the plates over to see where the critical information is and to scan for unusual features of the approach.

This way, when you're in the cockpit getting kicked around by turbulence you'll have an easier time of it when it comes time to set up for and shoot the approach.

In this section we'll take a look at a typically crowded approach plate and go through a step-by-step method for picking information off of it and flying the approach.

ILS Data Review

We're big on checklists, particularly well-designed ones. By breaking down a complex task into small pieces they can go a long way towards reducing error and making a pilot's life easier.

We use the checklist approach (no pun intended) when flying ILSes to simplify the process of gathering information from the plate, then setting up for and flying the approach.

Here's an overview of how to go about picking data off the plate and flying the approach.

Many courses

Refer to the ILS RWY 6 for Dublin, Virginia. This procedure is a good one for reviewing data pick-off, equipment and procedure planning. Follow along with paper and pencil as we go through each variation step-by-step and think about how you would fly this approach in your airplane.

There are five initial approach fixes that can be used to transition to the final approach course. You could be assigned any one of them by Roanoke Approach.

Radar might not be available, so you should be prepared to fly this procedure on your own navigation from any fix. It won't be as difficult as it might appear once you've completed this exercise.

Follow each route

An instrument approach chart is like a road map that's designed to get you from point A to point B. It appears to be nothing more than a confusing bunch of lines until you pick a starting point and follow a route to your destination. In this case, each initial approach fix is a potential starting point. We'll begin by locating each IAF so we can determine the equipment needed and follow each route to the airport.

1. Location of initial approach fixes:
• Pulaski Vortac 341°R, 10 DME arc (southbound)
• Pulaski Vortac 153°R, 10 DME arc (northbound)
• Gunto Intersection
• Kland Intersection
• Maxme Intersection

2. Primary facility:
I-PSK localizer (108.9).

3. Supporting facilities:
• Pulaski (PSK) Vortac (116.8)
• Bluefield (BLF) Vortac (110.0)

4. Time to missed approach:
3:24 at 90 knots.

5. Straight-in and Circling minimums for all categories:
• DH - 2465 feet and 1 mile
• MDA - 2680 feet and 1 mile (straight-in); 2700 feet and 1 mile (circling
Categories A & B)

6. Procedure turns:
No procedure turn except when using Gunto Intersection as an IAF.

7. Missed approach:
Climb straight ahead to 3000 feet, then climbing right turn to 5000 feet
direct to PSK Vortac and hold, right turns.

Pulaski transition
If ATC clears you from Pulaski Vortac to Gunto Intersection, your
equipment set-up and route should be:

1. #1 nav (assuming this has glideslope): I-PSK localizer, OBS - 58°.

2. #2 nav: PSK Vortac, OBS - 245°, DME: Hold (this allows you to
continue receiving distance from PSK if you change frequencies).

3. Fly the 245°R at 5000 feet until intercepting the localizer.

4. After crossing Gunto, maintain 238° for one minute.

5. Turn right and intercept the localizer inbound, 058°.

6. After crossing Gunto inbound, descend to 3900 feet. Tune the #2 nav
to the localizer as a backup.

7. Slow to the landing gear extension speed (if applicable).

8. As the glideslope moves on scale, lower the gear and approach flaps
(in accordance with the POH). Slow to final approach speed.
Control the glideslope with pitch and the airspeed with power. This
results in smoothness and accuracy. During an ILS, the glideslope is
primary for pitch. Don't adjust the power unless the airspeed changes
five knots or more.

9. Note the time when passing Jesta so, if the glideslope fails, you can
maintain the MDA of 2680 feet and continue the localizer approach. If
you haven't timed yourself, you may have to initiate a missed approach

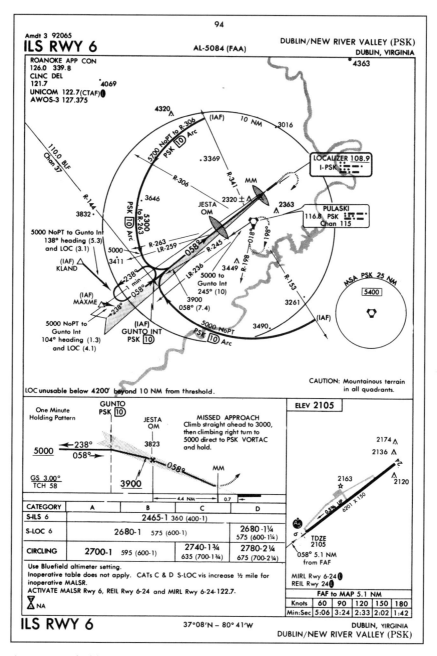

An approach like this one, with five initial approach fixes, might seem confusing at first. But, if you take each route separately and follow it from start to finish, it simplifies matters considerably.

if the glideslope fails.

10. Assuming everything is normal, follow the glideslope to DH. If one of the required visual references is not in sight at decision height, start a missed approach immediately. Don't be tempted into trying anything else, even if you catch a glimpse of the runway during the missed approach.

11. If a missed approach is necessary, climb straight ahead to 3000 feet, then turn right and continue climbing to 5000 feet direct PSK Vortac.

12. At PSK, make a parallel entry (198°) and after one minute, turn left to intercept the 018° inbound and turn right at the vortac to remain in the hold.

DME arc transition

1. #1 nav: I-PSK localizer, OBS - 58°.

2. #2 nav: PSK Vortac; OBS - 341°, DME Hold.

3. Fly the arc southwestbound at 5700 feet and make 10-degree heading changes to stay on the arc.

4. Reset the #2 nav to the 306° R.

5. Descend to 5300 feet after crossing the 306°R and reset the OBS to 263°.

6. Descend to 5000 feet after crossing the 263°R and reset the OBS to 259°.

7. Turn left to intercept the localizer when crossing the 259°R (a lead-in radial).

8. You should be inside Gunto when intercepting the localizer. If you're not inside Gunto, you must maintain 5000 feet. You can verify Gunto with the BLF 144°R. In this case, descend to 3900 feet and set the #2 nav to the localizer as a backup. Complete the approach as published.

Flying the routes from the remaining three initial approach fixes is similar.

Bit by bit

There are two things you should note about this exercise. First, that each individual step is small and easy to complete. At no time are you trying to think about too much at once.

The other pertinent point is that by using a step-by-step method of picking up data and putting it to use, you can stay ahead of the approach without worrying about whether you've missed something. Completing each step thoroughly (and making *sure* it's complete before moving on) allows you to think about what's next. (There's a glib expression we heard once, that the most important two things about flying instruments are the *next two things.*)

A checklist, of course, can also come in the form of an acronym. Aviation is full of these, and everybody has his or her favorite. One we've found useful for flying instrument approaches is I SHAFT'M, which was cooked up by one of our contributing editors. It works for any kind of approach.

Approach Chart Checklist

One of us works at a simulator training center and one of our tasks is to instruct pilots in instrument procedures. Until a few years ago, almost all the pilots we trained were members of two-pilot flight crews. In these operations, setting up for an instrument approach is usually accomplished by using a checklist, with one pilot reading and doing while the other pilot flies.

Then we started training more single-pilot operators. One of the first things we noticed was the single-pilot operator seldom used an approach checklist and, consequently, the approach set up was often haphazard. Some pilots would start at the top of the approach chart and work their way down, often missing critical pieces of information while dwelling on minutia. Others would choose random pieces of information from the chart, setting up for the approach in no particular order and sometimes missing key elements.

This experience encouraged us to develop an acronym that could be easily remembered, yet would help ensure the critical parts of the approach setup were accomplished. The result was the acronym **I SHAFT'M.** Although it isn't completely fool proof (common sense is still required) I'SHAFT'M has proved over and over to be an effective aid.

I SHAFT'M can be used either as a checklist to set up for an instrument approach or it can be used as a done checklist. A "done" checklist is used after the setup has been accomplished from memory, to ensure no critical items have been missed.

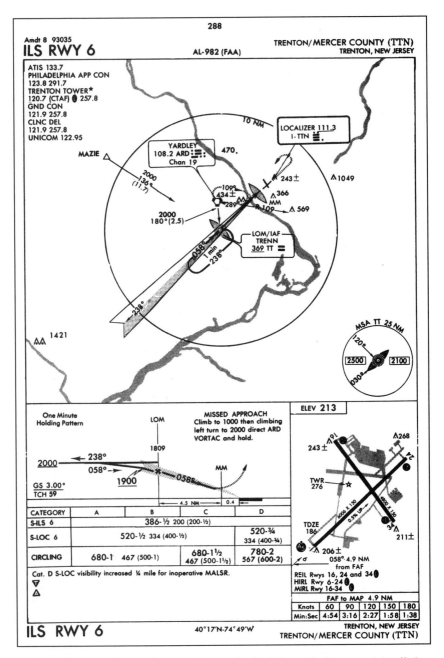

I SHAFT'M can be used as an approach checklist to help you pick off the important information from the chart of as a "done" checklist to ensure no critical items have been missed.

The I SHAFT'M approach checklist:

Identify - Identify the correct approach chart.
Speed - Decide on speed to maintain on final approach.
HSI - Set inbound approach course in course selector.
Altitudes - Review successive altitudes. Set DH/MDA.
Frequencies - Tune all navaids. Review/tune com frequencies.
Timing - Note time/DME to missed approach point. Zero the clock.
Missed - Review procedure, set required navaids.

Let's use I SHAFT'M to set up for the Trenton, Mercer County ILS RWY 6.

Identify

Step one in the approach setup is to IDENTIFY the correct instrument approach procedure (IAP) for the approach being flown. Unless this step is correctly accomplished, the remainder of the approach setup is in vain.

There are numerous examples in both the training environment and the real world of pilots setting up for the wrong approach, sometimes with tragic consequences.

For example, there are often approaches in the same geographic area with similar titles:
• The LDA DME 18 and the Rosslyn LDA 18, both at Washington National.
• The New York ILS DME 13 at La Guardia and the New York ILS 13L at Kennedy.
• The New York ILS 22 at La Guardia and the New York ILS 22R at Kennedy.
• Several pages before the ILS Runway 6 for Trenton (in the NOS approach book) is the ILS Runway 6 for Teterboro, NJ.

It isn't difficult to imagine, especially in a heavy workload environment, confusing these similar sounding approaches. In fact, each example above is from mistakes we've seen professional pilots make in a flight simulator.

So, the first step in the approach setup is to always ensure the correct approach chart has been *identified*.

Speed

Predetermining the speed to fly the approach is important for several reasons:
1. Precision flying requires good airspeed control. In order to fly an

instrument approach and use the techniques outlined in the FAA Instrument Flying Handbook (AC 61-27C), airspeed must be maintained. For example, the ATP flight test sets acceptable airspeed variations during an approach at +5/-0 knots.

2. Airspeed must be maintained so as to remain witin the appropriate category minimums to ensure obstacle clearance in the event of a missed approach.

Reviewing the Trenton ILS 6, the DH and minimum visibility are the same for all categories, however category D minimums increase for the straight-in localizer approach. Also, circling minimums increase for both category C and D airspeeds.

3. Since timing is necessary during most approaches, a constant groundspeed must be maintained to ensure accuracy in locating the MAP.

For these reasons, determine the speed at which you'll fly the approach and maintain it.

HSI

Before beginning an approach, familiarize yourself with the inbound final approach course. Doing so enhances situational awareness. Situational awareness is knowing where you are and where you're going in relation to both the instrument approach and the terrain. In this respect, an HSI (Horizontal Situation Indicator) is a tremendous tool. For the ILS 6 at Trenton, set the inbound course of 58 degrees in the HSI course selector window. By doing this, you have an instant graphic on the HSI of the approach plan view, and the aircraft's relationship to it.

If your aircraft isn't equipped with an HSI, the word HEADING can be substituted. Although it takes a little more work, acquaint yourself with the inbound final approach course heading for improved situational awareness relative to the approach.

Altitudes

Altitude awareness is the heart of IFR flying. Review the minimum altitudes for the expected route of flight. For example, you're 15 miles north of Yardley Vortac and receive the following clearance:

"Cleared direct Yardley, maintain 3000. After crossing Yardley, cleared for the Trenton ILS Runway 6 approach. Report procedure turn inbound."

The first altitude you should review is the minimum safe altitude (MSA), which in this case is in the lower right corner of the plan view. Although the MSA is published for emergency use only, use it to raise your situational awareness. The MSA 15 miles north of Yardley is 2100 feet, which provides 1000 feet of obstruction clearance.

A further review of the plan view shows that the first altitude change after the vortac is on the feeder route from Yardley to Trenn LOM. This transition is 2.5 miles on the 180 radial at a minimum altitude of 2000 feet. Since you've been cleared for the approach after crossing the vortac, you can descend to 2000 feet once established on this route.

The profile view shows that after crossing the LOM outbound, the minimum altitude for the racetrack course reversal remains at 2000 feet. When inbound on the localizer, you can descend and maintain 1900 feet until glideslope intercept.

According to the profile view, you should cross the LOM on the glideslope at 1809 feet msl. This information can be used to guard against following a false glideslope and to ensure the altimeter is reading correctly.

Finally, the glideslope will reach decision height at 386 feet msl, which is 200 feet above the touchdown zone. Decision height is probably the single most important altitude on the approach chart and should be either set in an altitude reminder or memorized. During nearly all phases of an IFR flight, you're assured a minimum obstacle clearance of at least 1000 feet (when at published altitudes). However, at decision height, you could be a mere 200 feet above the ground and, at a 120 knots, descending at 635 feet per minute!

Frequencies

All navigational frequencies associated with this approach should now be tuned and identified. Communication frequencies should also be reviewed and if possible set. The primary navaid for the approach is the localizer. The frequency 111.3 is underlined, indicating no voice is transmitted on this frequency.

Other important navaids include the Yardley Vortac on 108.2. Yardley, unlike the localizer has DME capability. This is indicated by the tacan channel. Trenn LOM should be tuned and identified, and a bearing pointer slaved to it. An LOM, when available, provides an important aid to situational awareness on any ILS. The last navaid to consider is the marker beacon. The audio should be on and the receiver should be in the low sense position.

A review of the communications frequencies in the upper left corner of the plan view is now in order. It's important to note that Trenton Tower doesn't operate continuously (indicated by the star) and some of the airport lighting is pilot-controlled when the tower is closed. This is indicated by the L next to the tower/common traffic advisory frequency (CTAF).

Timing

Although timing isn't required for an ILS approach, it's a way to determine the missed approach point if the glideslope fails. If timing is part of the approach, you must compute an estimated groundspeed for the final approach segment. Use your predetermined airspeed minus any headwind component. Note the time required for the approach on the lower right corner of the chart is 2:27 at 120 knots. Zero the clock and be prepared to start it at the FAF inbound.

If timing isn't a required part of an approach, determine where the missed approach point (MAP) is and how to establish it. Typically, the last fix on the profile view will be the navaid or DME fix for the missed approach when timing is either not required or alternate means of identifying the MAP are available.

Missed approach

Review the missed approach and set up for it as necessary. Some instructors believe the only part of the missed approach that should be memorized is the first line, e.g., Climb to 1000', while the rest of the procedure can be reread after a climb has been established. Other pilots feel strongly that the entire procedure must be committed to memory prior to initiating the approach, especially if the weather is at or near minimums.

We've observed pilots get so engrossed in reading the missed approach procedure while flying the missed approach that they actually flew into the ground. Fortunately, this occurred in a flight simulator. The experience prompted us to review missed approach procedures. Until recently, we were convinced that every missed approach narrative began with the letters C-L-I-M-B. The other day someone showed me a missed approach that began *"Immediately climb."*

So, even if you forget the missed approach procedure or you never read it, rest assured that a climb is always the first order of business.

Useful for all operations

I SHAFT'M works well for many pilots, especially in single-pilot operations. One commercial operator created a written form with the initials and key words of the I SHAFT'M acronym. Each pilot keeps this form on the kneeboard for use in IFR approach setups.

I SHAFT'M doesn't include specific reference to some of the details and notes that appear on the approach charts. A thorough review of these details and notes is recommended. For example, on the Trenton

ILS, the category D straight-in localizer visibility minimum increases one-quarter mile if the MALSR is inoperative.

Hopefully, I SHAFT'M will be a worthwhile companion during an instrument approach. You can modify it to meet your particular style and needs.

One example of arcane symbology has to do with airport equipment codes. Here's a look at the various codes you'll find regarding an airport's VASI equipment and its equivalents.

Approach Slope Lights

NOS chart users who've been around for more than about five years may have noticed some unfamiliar lighting symbols on the airport diagram. If you're not sure what they mean, it's time for a review. This symbology exists to account for the different types of VASIs now in service, such as PAPI, PVASI and T-VASI. As with any approach light system, it's important to know the type of VASI to look for and how to interpret it.

Under the old lighting symbology, a V indicated that a VASI was installed, but did not indicate which of the six types presently in service was used. The V now indicates that a standard two-bar VASI is used with either a two, four or twelve light system. Regardless of the number of lights in the system, you will see the standard colors indicating too high, on glide slope or too low.

A VL indicates a three-bar VASI with a threshold crossing height to accommodate long-body or jumbo aircraft. Remember, if you're not flying one of these aircraft, you'll have a choice of two aim points for touchdown since a jumbo or wide-body uses the far set for touchdown.

PAPI

The precision approach path indicator (PAPI) is indicated by P. PAPI is a four-light system installed to the left of the runway. If the lights are all white, you're higher than a 3.5 degree approach path. One red light indicates a slightly high approach (3.2 degrees). Two reds and two whites is a 3.0 degree approach path. Three reds is slightly low (2.8 degrees) and all red indicates less than 2.5 degrees.

T-VASI

A V1 indicates that a T-VASI is installed on both sides of the runway. With this VASI, you will see either an inverted T, a single bar across, or

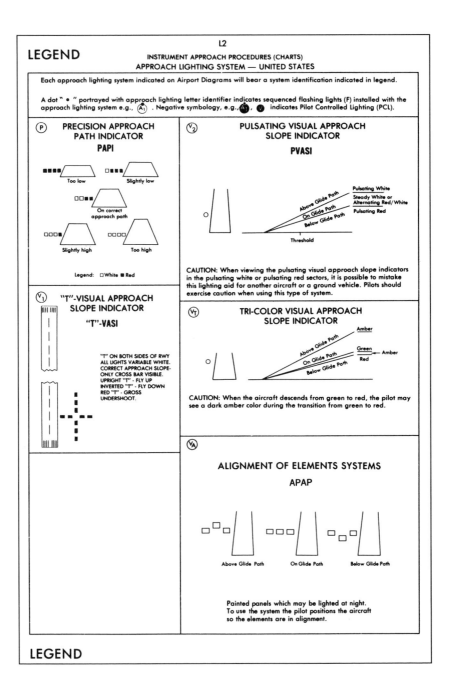

LEGEND

INSTRUMENT APPROACH PROCEDURES (CHARTS)
APPROACH LIGHTING SYSTEM — UNITED STATES

Each approach lighting system indicated on Airport Diagrams will bear a system identification indicated in legend.

A dot " • " portrayed with approach lighting letter identifier indicates sequenced flashing lights (F) installed with the approach lighting system e.g., (A₁) . Negative symbology, e.g., (A₁), (V) indicates Pilot Controlled Lighting (PCL).

(P) PRECISION APPROACH PATH INDICATOR
PAPI

Too low
Slightly low
On correct approach path
Slightly high
Too high

Legend: □ White ■ Red

(V₁) "T"-VISUAL APPROACH SLOPE INDICATOR
"T"-VASI

"T" ON BOTH SIDES OF RWY ALL LIGHTS VARIABLE WHITE. CORRECT APPROACH SLOPE-ONLY CROSS BAR VISIBLE. UPRIGHT "T" - FLY UP INVERTED "T" - FLY DOWN RED "T" - GROSS UNDERSHOOT.

(V₂) PULSATING VISUAL APPROACH SLOPE INDICATOR
PVASI

Above Glide Path — Pulsating White
On Glide Path — Steady White or Alternating Red/White
Below Glide Path — Pulsating Red
Threshold

CAUTION: When viewing the pulsating visual approach slope indicators in the pulsating white or pulsating red sectors, it is possible to mistake this lighting aid for another aircraft or a ground vehicle. Pilots should exercise caution when using this type of system.

(Vᴛ) TRI-COLOR VISUAL APPROACH SLOPE INDICATOR

Above Glide Path — Amber
On Glide Path — Green ← Amber
Below Glide Path — Red

CAUTION: When the aircraft descends from green to red, the pilot may see a dark amber color during the transition from green to red.

(Vᴀ)

ALIGNMENT OF ELEMENTS SYSTEMS
APAP

Above Glide Path
On Glide Path
Below Glide Path

Painted panels which may be lighted at night. To use the system the pilot positions the aircraft so the elements are in alignment.

LEGEND

an upright T.

An inverted T with three lights on top indicates that you're very high. A straight bar across means you're on a 3.0-degree approach. An upright T of any kind indicates you're low, and three lights on the bottom indicates very low. The lights are always white unless you're well below glide path, in which case you'll see all red.

Single-Light Systems

A pulsating visual approach slope indicator (PVASI) uses a pulsating light to indicate when you're too high (white) or too low (red). A steady white or alternating red/white is an on glide path indication. This system is indicated by V2. Its useful range is four miles during the day and up to ten miles at night.

Finally, the tricolor VASI (VT) uses red, green and amber for its indications instead of the usual red and white combination. Green indicates you're on glide path. Amber indicates high and red indicates low. This system has a useful range of one-half to one mile during the day and up to five miles at night. The effective range of the normal VASIs and PAPI is five miles during the day and up to 20 miles at night. Obstacle clearance is provided within plus or minus ten degrees of the extended runway centerline and out to four nautical miles from the runway threshold.

For confusing, tough-to-remember symbols, few things beat the NOS depiction of an airport's pilot controlled lighting (PCL).

While all pilots know (or should know) that in order to use PCL a pilot keys the mic on a given frequency several times, there are several twists to the way the systems work that are not so obvious.

Here's a look at the many nuances of pilot-controlled lighting systems, both standard and non-standard.

Pilot-Controlled Lighting

The pilot of the Cessna 210 was cleared for the ILS to Runway 36 at Savannah, GA. Since it was late night and the tower had long since closed, the pilot knew he would have to activate the runway lights by clicking the mic on the tower frequency. He dutifully clicked the mic seven times in order to have the approach lights blazing when he broke out. Imagine his surprise upon breaking out at 300 feet, only to find a black hole where the runway was supposed to be.

Instead of illuminating his approach path, the pilot had activated the lights on Runway 9/27. Why? Because the tower had selected the active runway before closing and the remote activation system would only work on the runway selected. Unfortunately, it didn't coincide with the runway to which the pilot wanted to shoot an approach.

Widely misunderstood

This true incident points out the misunderstanding pilots have about airport lighting systems and the lack of standardization among each system.

Ever since the various energy crises of the 1970s, airport operators have been much more aggressive about saving money on the monthly lighting tab. You certainly can't blame them for not wanting to have every airport light blazing away for the entire night. The result has been a proliferation in the number of pilot controlled lighting (PCL) systems.

Do you know the difference between a standard and non-standard PCL system or how many times to click the mic for various lighting intensities? How long do the lights remain on after activation? Now more than ever, you need to do your homework before filing IFR to an unattended airport at night. It could mean the difference between making a successful approach and having to divert to an alternate.

A runway served by an instrument approach can have a combination of low, medium and high intensity runway lights (LIRL, MIRL and HIRL); runway end identifier lights (REIL); visual approach slope indicator (VASI) and approach lights. With a PCL system, ordinarily these lights can be adjusted in three steps by clicking the mic three, five or seven times.

Standard PCL systems

What happens to the lights after you click depends on whether the runway has approach lights and the level to which the system is set. The charts shown here (from the AIM) illustrate the differences in each *standard* system.

Figure 1 shows how you can adjust the lighting intensity on a runway with approach lights. By clicking the mic seven times, you get the brightest approach lights, but the runway lights are set to a predetermined level. So you might or might not get the highest level available for the runway itself. This could be critical during low visibility when visual cues from the runway are needed most.

Figure 2 lists the intensity levels for runways without approach lights. Regardless of the system, clicking the mic seven times gives you the highest level. Some systems allow you to adjust the intensity up or down by using three, five or seven clicks. The lights remain on 15 minutes after activation.

Non-standard systems

The features of non-standard PCL systems vary and might or might not work according to the guidelines in Figures 1 and 2. For example, one system requires that you click the mic five times for medium intensity runway lights, taxiway lights and REIL. You click three more times for high intensity lights and the lights blink two minutes before turning off (the proverbial two-minute warning). Some non-standard systems operate on a frequency other than the unicom or tower.

A standard PCL system is noted by an "L" on the airport diagram of NOS approach charts. An "L*" denotes a non-standard system, in which case you'll need to refer to the Airport/Facility Directory (A/FD) to find out how it works. If you use Jeppesen charts, PCL instructions are listed on the airport diagram page.

Refer to the A/FD or equivalent publication to review lighting information and avoid embarrassment. In the case of the pilot flying into Savannah, the approach chart indicates that a standard PCL system is available. However, when the A/FD is reviewed, you'll find the following notation, "When tower closed activate runway and approach lights for predetermined favorable runway on CTAF." It'll be tough sledding if you want to shoot an approach to the non-favored runway.

When possible, find out the favored runway from approach control. The peculiarities of this system aren't discernible from the approach chart. The A/FD must be reviewed to get the rest of the story.

We seldom think about how critical the approach and runway lights are to a successful approach. Most pilots only worry about the approach lights increasing the visibility minimum during the day. At night, it's a whole different story. Imagine shooting an approach to a remote airport and having to divert to an alternate miles away because you can't use the lights!

Figure 1 - PCL for Runways With Approach Lights

Lighting System	Steps	Normal stat.	3 clicks	5 clicks	7 clicks
Appch. Lights (med)	2	Off	Low	Low	High
Appch Lights (med)	3	Off	Low	Med	High
MIRL	3	Off or Low	Preset	Preset	Preset
HIRL	5	Off or Low	Preset	Preset	Preset
VASI	2	Off	Preset	Preset	Preset

Figure 2 - PCL for Runways Without Approach Lights

Lighting System	Steps	Normal stat.	3 clicks	5 clicks	7 clicks
MIRL	3	Off or Low	Low	Med	High
HIRL	5	Off or Low	Step 1 or 2	Step 3	Step 5
LIRL	1	Off	On	On	On
VASI	2	Off	Preset	Preset	Preset
REIL	1	Off	Off	On/Off	On
REIL	3	Off	Low	Med	High

Here's a puzzler that should test your chart reading skills. It's a good example of why you should review the plates for your destination during your flight planning activity, rather than waiting until you're in the cockpit, up to your eyeballs in cruddy weather and turbulence.

Case History: Is This Chart Correct?

Here's the challenge: Quickly review the approach chart for the VOR Runway 33 at Roanoke Regional on the next page. (Don't read further until you've examined it.)

Now, here's the question. What is the *minimum* equipment needed to execute this procedure without ATC assistance?

If you said VOR only, you're wrong. If you answered ADF only, wrong again. Those of you who answered VOR *and* ADF passed with flying colors. Don't feel bad if it took you a while to find the answer. It isn't obvious and a lot of pilots miss this one.

Procedure mislabeled?

If you examine the chart closely, you'll find the notation, "ADF required." Sure enough, the NDB is the final approach fix and it cannot be identified by any other method.

A quick glance at the profile view of the chart can be misleading, since the descent to the procedure turn is shown from the NDB, not the VOR. The NDB is also an initial approach fix, which can lead to further confusion.

The obvious question is, "Shouldn't this procedure be labeled a VOR/NDB approach instead of a VOR only?" Doing so would prompt you to look further in the event you failed to observe the "ADF required" note.

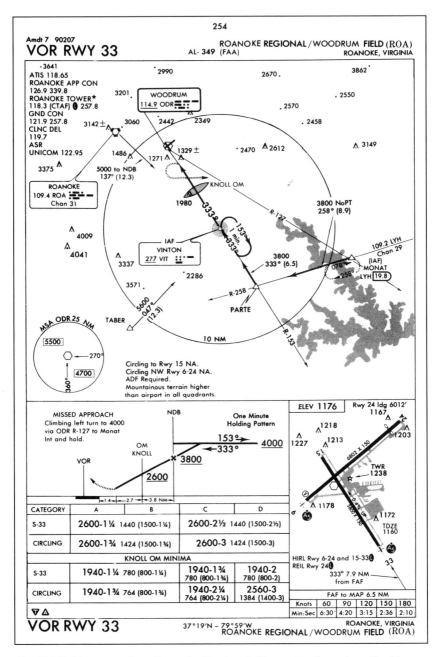

The VOR 33 approach at Roanoke Regional illustrates the value of asking a simple question: How do I fly this?

Correctly identified

At first glance, this procedure seems to be a quirk in the system that the FAA uses to classify approach procedures. However, the procedure is classified correctly according to FAA Advisory Circular AC 90-1, "Civil Use of U.S. Government Instrument Approach Procedure Charts."

The Advisory Circular states that, "The procedure identification is derived from the type facility providing final approach course guidance...." Since the VOR is the only facility providing final approach course guidance for this procedure, the NDB requirement is not included in the title.

Outer marker helps

Although it isn't required to fly the approach, the outer marker is an integral part of this procedure. Category A, B, and C aircraft can descend to 780 feet agl if the Knoll outer marker can be identified during a straight-in approach. This is 660 feet lower than the straight-in MDA without Knoll, which is a substantial difference. This seemingly simple VOR approach requires several pieces of equipment in order to descend to the lowest minimums.

Other considerations

Another item that requires close scrutiny is the minimum safe altitude (MSA). Since this is a VOR approach, you might assume that the MSA is based on the VOR used for the procedure, however, the Vinton NDB is used. Notice that the MSA is quite high from the NDB to the airport. You only need to look at the elevation numbers northwest of the airport to understand why. This also accounts for the fact that circling approaches are not permitted northwest of Runway 06/24 or to Runway 15.

The missed approach procedure also indicates that obstacle clearance is a problem in the vicinity of the airport. This procedure requires a climbing left turn away from the airport and back over the final approach course until intercepting the VOR radial.

Before beginning any approach, review all the navaids listed on the chart and determine if you'll need them to fly the approach to the lowest published minimums. Then be sure to tune and identify each facility as soon as possible. In addition to the five Ts, remember the five Ps: Prior Planning Prevents Poor Performance.

Let's take another look at equipment notes on charts. Usually, the reasoning behind a given equipment requirement is evident from examining the chart closely. Sometimes, though, the equipment requirements arise from some obscure regulation or simply because the requirement will facilitate ATC's job.

Minimum Equipment Requirements

An instrument student we know, having been unexpectedly assigned a VOR/DME approach cluttered with stepdown fixes and cautionary notes, was feeling a bit overwhelmed.

"How do they expect you to read all this stuff and fly the airplane at the same time?" he asked.

It's a good question for which we have no ready answer other than to say that *they*—being the Feds, your instructor and your passengers—do expect you to be able to read a plate's fine print while holding heading and altitude and yapping on the radio at the same time. Moreover, before you even accept an approach, you're supposed to know what navigation equipment is required to fly it.

As specific (and restrictive) as the FARs are on other topics, the equipment requirements for IFR flight are, to put it kindly, nebulous. The relevant reg is FAR 91.205. It says that you're required to have "navigational equipment appropriate to the ground facilities to be used."

Take that logic to its bitter end and you'll conclude (rightly) that all you need for IFR flight in your 1964 Cessna 150 is a comm radio and a single VOR. Or, if NDBs are your thing, forget the VOR, fly from beacon to beacon and shoot an NDB at your destination. Nothing in 91.205 says you can't do just that, as long as you avoid airspace where a transponder is required. (Anyone who manages to fast-talk ATC into going along with this will kindly fax us a copy of the clearance.)

Suppose, however, that the approach you want to fly has a fix defined by a crossing radial. Shouldn't you have dual VOR to fix the intersection? That's definitely the best way but it's not required; if you can identify the intersection with one VOR, you're legal, at least most of the time. Some approaches, such as the two we've selected this month, do require dual VORs or other special equipment, a fact that should be noted on the plate.

Other than the dogleg final at the FAF, the VOR 6 into Toms River, N.J., is quite ordinary. Look closely at the profile view and you'll see the special equipment note: "Dual VOR or VOR & DME required for Palet Int." Does that mean that our imaginary single-VOR Cessna can't accept the approach? Not really. It just means that in order to descend

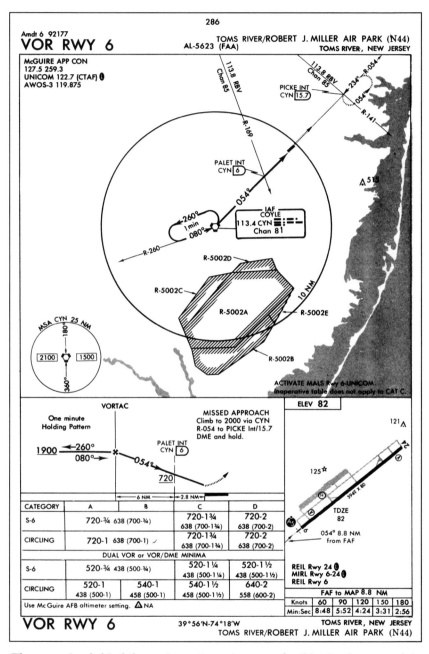

286

Amdt 6 92177

VOR RWY 6

TOMS RIVER/ROBERT J. MILLER AIR PARK (N44)
AL-5623 (FAA)
TOMS RIVER, NEW JERSEY

McGUIRE APP CON
127.5 259.3
UNICOM 122.7 (CTAF) ◐
AWOS-3 119.875

The reasoning behind the equipment requirements for this simple approach is not obvious. It arises from a "gotcha" in the TERPS.

to the lowest available MDA, 520 feet in this case, we'll have to identify PALET with dual VOR or DME.

The reason for this so-called dual MDA is an obscure TERPS provision called the excessive length of final penalty. This rule requires that the lowest available MDA be raised 5 feet for every .1 mile that the final approach segment exceeds 6 miles. In this case, the penalty is 140 feet, plus another 60-foot penalty for lack of a local altimeter setting.

Thus, by having dual VOR or VOR and DME, you gain a 200-foot credit. Without it, your MDA is 720 feet. On NOS charts, by the way, there's no separate note about the equipment requirement. Instead, a dual minimums box gives lower-MDA credit for PALET. Fine print in the box explains that PALET must be identified with dual VOR or DME.

One tip: Whenever dual minima exist, check the other approaches carefully as well. At Toms River, the ILS has dual minimums too, but they only apply to a local charter operator with approved weather reporting. The difference is a 50-foot lower DH and this would be easy to miss in a dark cockpit.

At major terminals, it's not uncommon to have both equipment requirements and a radar requirement, as is the case for the converging ILS/DME-2 17L at Denver's Stapleton Airport. The reason for radar is obvious. There's no procedure turn and no transition routes. Radar vectoring is the only way to get into the approach.

Less obvious is the requirement for simultaneous reception of the 17L localizer and the Denver VORTAC's DME signal. In flying the approach, you can identify the FAF at glideslope intercept; the MAP occurs at DH on the glideslope. There's no outer marker or LOM but since there's no LOC version of this approach anyway, these aren't needed for the non-precision final approach fix.

The DME requirement is there primarily for ATC convenience. DEEPE and the DEN 13 fix are routinely assigned as crossing restrictions, so a pilot needs DME to identify the fixes. Also, TARGS, a fix in lieu of a marker, is the usual tower handoff point.

The converging ILS 17L/ILS 8R is used often at Denver because the airport lies at the confluence of two uncomplementary phenomena: a lot of airplanes and a lot of bad weather. Just about every weekday morning, arrivals inundate Denver but there are few departures. When the weather is too poor to use parallel approaches, controllers switch to the converging procedures that were approved several years ago.

Converging approaches have relatively high minimums (a 440-foot HAT and 1 mile in this case) and they do require delicate coordination between tower and TRACON, but at an airport like Denver, they considerably increase runway capacity. The 17L converging ILS is

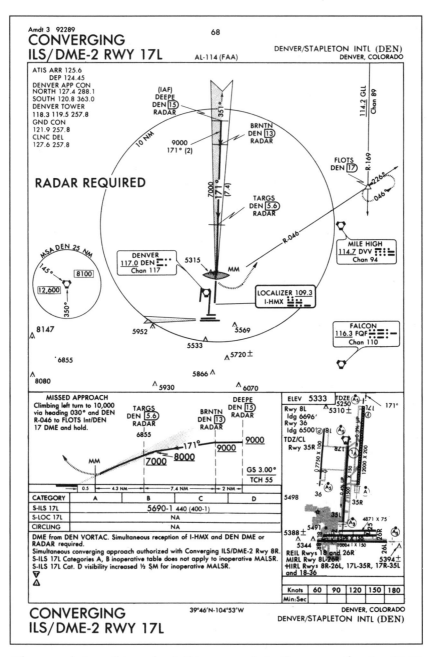

The non-obvious thing about this approach is the reason for the DME requirement, since it's not actually needed to fly the approach.

always used with the 8R ILS. That's why the localizer feather projects from the end of runway 8, to give pilots a sense of where the converging traffic is coming from.

The runways are 12,000 feet and 10,000 feet respectively, so fast air carrier traffic gets assigned to both ILSs. That means that any general aviation airplanes (including our DME-equipped Cessna 150) will get slotted on the localizer between a couple of heavies and will probably be asked to maintain the highest possible speed until crossing the marker or the tower handoff fix. But if you've flown into air-carrier terminals before, that shouldn't be a problem. Hold a high power setting and fly the airspeed needle in the middle of the green arc. You'll have plenty of time to slow down and more than enough runway to get stopped. Just watch out for that converging traffic if you have to shoot the missed.

When is a requirement not a requirement? Some approaches do require ATC radar but that doesn't always mean it has to be working in order for you to fly the procedure.

Radar Required

Wouldn't it be nice if someone would invent a device that could call back some dumb thing you've said over the radio? Of course, it would need various sensitivity settings. At the low end, you could use it to eliminate stutters, hesitations and the "aahhhh" syndrome. Set at max power, it would retrieve from the ether the Doomsday Transmission; the inadvertent utterance that instantly brands you as the hopeless idiot you've secretly feared you actually were.

A pilot we overhead recently would be a good customer for such a device. He was being vectored for the ILS 7 approach into Provincetown, Massachusetts, a small airport on the very tip of Cape Cod.

"Ah Cape approach, Cherokee One Two Three...it looks like we won't be able to do the approach. The plate says radar is required and all we have aboard is a Stormscope."

During the stony silence that followed, we imagine that two things happened in unison. The controller probably rolled his eyes and sighed and a nanosecond after he had unkeyed his mike, the pilot realized he had just suffered a massive brain fart.

"Sir," replied the controller, without a hint of impatience or sarcasm, "that note refers to *my* radar not yours. Descend to 3000 feet and fly

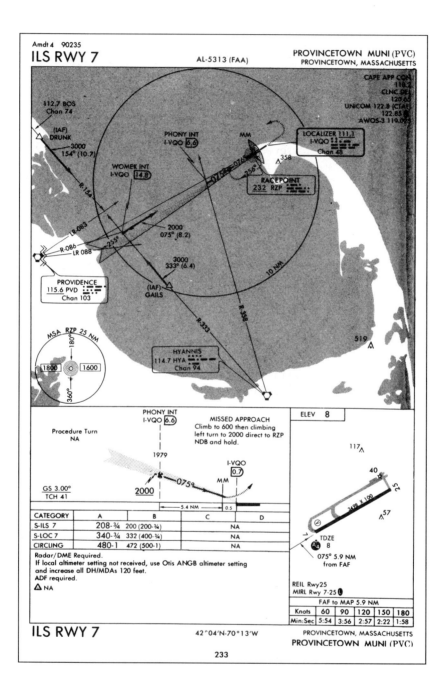

Amdt 4 90235

ILS RWY 7

AL-5313 (FAA)

PROVINCETOWN MUNI (PVC)
PROVINCETOWN, MASSACHUSETTS

CAPE APP CON
118.2
CLNC DEL
120.65
UNICOM 122.8 (CTAF)
122.85
AWOS-3 119.025

112.7 BOS
Chan 74

(IAF)
DRUNK

—3000
154° (10.7)

WOMEK INT
I-VQO 14.8

PHONY INT
I-VQO 6.6

MM

LOCALIZER 111.1
I-VQO
Chan 48

358

075° 075°
256°

RACEPOINT
232 RZP

R-144

LR 083

R-086
LR 088

255°

2000
075° (8.2)

3000
333° (6.4)

10 NM

PROVIDENCE
115.6 PVD
Chan 103

(IAF)
GAILS

R-333

R-358

MSA RZP 25 NM
180°
1800 · 1600
360°

HYANNIS
114.7 HYA
Chan 94

519

PHONY INT
I-VQO 6.6

MISSED APPROACH
Climb to 600 then climbing
left turn to 2000 direct to RZP
NDB and hold.

ELEV 8

Procedure Turn
NA

1979

I-VQO
0.7

MM

117

40
25

GS 3.00°
TCH 41

2000

075°

348 X 100

57

5.4 NM   0.5

7

TDZE
8

CATEGORY	A	B	C	D
S-ILS 7	208-¾	200 (200-¾)	NA	
S-LOC 7	340-¾	332 (400-¾)	NA	
CIRCLING	480-1	472 (500-1)	NA	

075° 5.9 NM
from FAF

Radar/DME Required.
If local altimeter setting not received, use Otis ANGB altimeter setting
and increase all DH/MDAs 120 feet.
ADF required.
⚠ NA

REIL Rwy25
MIRL Rwy 7-25

FAF to MAP 5.9 NM					
Knots	60	90	120	150	180
Min:Sec	5:54	3:56	2:57	2:22	1:58

ILS RWY 7

42°04'N-70°13'W

PROVINCETOWN, MASSACHUSETTS
PROVINCETOWN MUNI (PVC)

heading 020, vectors for the ILS 7 at Provincetown."

"Ahhh..yeah, roger," came the weak reply from the pilot.

In all fairness, the pilot's confusion is somewhat understandable. Notes on plates that call for special equipment or that describe out-of-the-ordinary limitations on a procedure can be perplexing, to say the least. The two plates we've printed here are typical examples.

Let's consider Provincetown first. In most respects, the ILS 7 is fairly ordinary. It has DME, a rather normal GS intercept altitude and, owing to the existence of approach lights, minimums that are quite low for an non-tower airport. However, notice that Provincetown is missing one thing: a procedure turn.

We weren't able to determine exactly why this is so. Usually, PT-less ILSs exist at major terminals, where traffic is routinely radar vectored to final or at airports where constructing a procedure turn might encroach on a nearby airport's turf. But traffic-wise, Provincetown is hardly DFW and it's so far out in the sticks that we can't imagine how a procedure turn could interfere with any neighboring airspace.

We couldn't find any particular reason for Provincetown not having a PT; it just doesn't. As for radar, it's normally required when there are no transitions from the airways structure into the approach or when there's no other way to identify a fix required for the approach. That's not the case at P-town, either. So what gives? Beats us. We suspect the radar note is a carry over from the days when Provincetown may not have had transitions of any kind.

One thing worth mentioning is the note itself. It's phrased "Radar/ DME required," suggesting that both are needed, not one or the other. We can see the reason for radar, but why the DME? You can fly both the ILS and the LOC version without DME. On the ILS, the FAF is glideslope intercept and the missed approach point is DA on the glideslope. For the LOC, the FAF can be fixed with either DME or a crossing radial from Hyannis VOR and the missed can be timed or identified with DME.

The answer to this dilemma is that the note is mistaken. It should read: Radar *or* DME required.

The note is correctly presented on the ILS 36L at Huntsville. It says "ADF *or* Radar required." Why the ADF? You need it to navigate to the missed approach holding fix at Capshaw, north of the field. Look closely, too, at the transitions for this approach. There's only one; it goes from the Rocket VOR to Capshaw, thence outbound to the IAF at WHEAL intersection. You need an ADF to fly that transition.

Fine. Suppose your ADF is inop but the local ASR-9 radar is working normally. If you accept the approach and have to miss, how are you

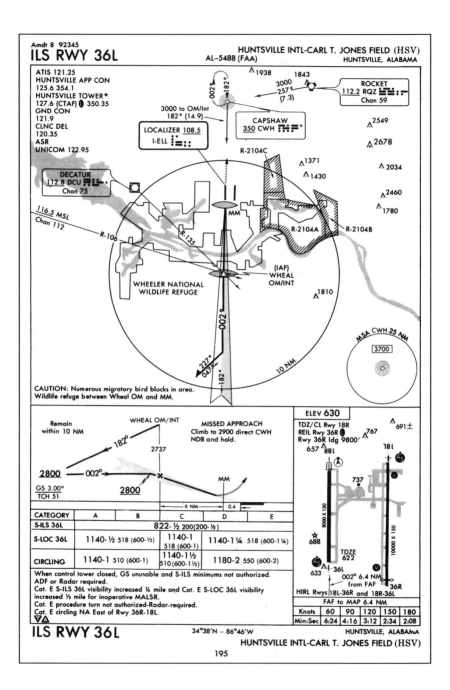

Amdt 8 92345

ILS RWY 36L

HUNTSVILLE INTL-CARL T. JONES FIELD (HSV)
AL–5488 (FAA)
HUNTSVILLE, ALABAMA

ATIS 121.25
HUNTSVILLE APP CON
125.6 354.1
HUNTSVILLE TOWER*
127.6 (CTAF) ● 350.35
GND CON
121.9
CLNC DEL
120.35
ASR
UNICOM 122.95

ROCKET
112.2 RQZ
Chan 59

CAPSHAW
350 CWH

LOCALIZER 108.5
I-ELL

3000 to OM/Int
182° (14.9)

DECATUR
112.8 DCU
Chan 75

116.5 MSL
Chan 112

R-106

R-135

R-2104C

R-2104A

R-2104B

MM

WHEELER NATIONAL
WILDLIFE REFUGE

(IAF)
WHEAL
OM/INT

MSA CWH 25 NM
3700

CAUTION: Numerous migratory bird blocks in area.
Wildlife refuge between Wheal OM and MM.

Remain
within 10 NM

WHEAL OM/INT

MISSED APPROACH
Climb to 2900 direct CWH
NDB and hold.

2737

2800 — 002°

2800

GS 3.00°
TCH 51

MM

ELEV 630
TDZ/CL Rwy 18R
REIL Rwy 36R ●
Rwy 36R ldg 9800'
657

691±
767
881

737

18L

A6

688

TDZE
622

633

A6

36L

002° 6.4 NM
from FAF
36R

HIRL Rwys 18L-36R and 18R-36L

CATEGORY	A	B	C	D	E
S-ILS 36L	822-½ 200(200-½)				
S-LOC 36L	1140-½ 518 (600-½)		1140-1 518 (600-1)	1140-1¼ 518 (600-1¼)	
CIRCLING	1140-1 510 (600-1)		1140-1½ 510 (600-1½)	1180-2 550 (600-2)	

When control tower closed, GS unusable and S-ILS minimums not authorized.
ADF or Radar required.
Cat. E S-ILS 36L visibility increased ¼ mile and Cat. E S-LOC 36L visibility
increased ½ mile for inoperative MALSR.
Cat. E procedure turn not authorized-Radar-required.
Cat. E circling NA East of Rwy 36R-18L.

FAF to MAP 6.4 NM

Knots	60	90	120	150	180
Min:Sec	6:24	4:16	3:12	2:34	2:08

ILS RWY 36L

34°38'N – 86°46'W

HUNTSVILLE, ALABAMA
HUNTSVILLE INTL-CARL T. JONES FIELD (HSV)

195

expected to navigate to Capshaw? Obviously, you can't but since radar is available, you can expect vectors after the missed approach.

Technically, there should be a formal alternate missed approach procedure which the controller is supposed to issue before you commence the approach, to cover all the bases in the event of lost comm. However, Huntsville doesn't have an alternate missed approach for the ILS 36L. So if your radios go away, you're on your own. If getting into Huntsville seemed unlikely, we would head for Muscle Shoals. It has an ILS with pilot nav transitions.

There are a couple of other oddities on these two approaches worth noting. Looking again at Provincetown, note that the transitions from GAILS and DRUNK intersections join the localizer at steep angles. The route from DRUNK (awful intersection name) joins the localizer at an 82-degree angle, the route from GAILS joins at an acute 102 degrees.

Both of these transitions have lead radials which signal the pilot when localizer intercept is about to occur. It's up to the pilot to decide when to actually commence the turn onto the localizer but if the wind is little or no factor, a standard rate turn started at the point where the needle centers on the lead radial will usually work. Of course, if there's a strong head or tail wind, you'll have to adjust accordingly.

The missed approach procedure at P-town is also somewhat unusual in that the holding fix is practically at the middle marker. The Racepoint beacon is very near the point where you would actually begin the climb for the missed approach and if you were flying into a strong northeast wind (not unusual on the Cape), you could very easily be blown well past the beacon during the outbound turn.

Perhaps a more elegant way to enter the hold would be to simply parallel the localizer outbound on the north side for a mile or two, then turn south to intercept the localizer inbound on the way back to Racepoint. That strategy would also give you time to climb to the holding altitude before entering the racetrack.

Huntsville's ILS has another attention-getting note on the right side of the profile: "CAUTION: Numerous migratory bird flocks in area. Wildlife refuge between OM & MM." Now there's a real thrill for you! Pop out of the clouds 200 feet above DA and scare the bejesus out of 10,000 mallards. Gives new meaning to the phrase "duck under," eh?

For our final topic on detailed chart reading, we'll step away from approach plates and take a look at en route charts. There's a lot of information on an en route chart that many pilots don't take advantage of simply because they're not sure how to find it.

A good example of this is the frequency listing for flight service. Taking advantage of the services provided by FSS can enhance your safety and make your trip more convenient, but to contact them you need to know how to find the right frequency on the chart. Naturally NOS and Jeppesen go about depicting frequencies differently.

Finding the Right Frequency

When the world outside the cockpit no longer resembles your preflight briefing, it's time to call flight service for an update.

The common FSS frequency is 122.2 MHz. Since almost every FSS uses this frequency, it's often congested due to interference from adjacent areas. Filing a flight plan or getting a complete weather briefing on this frequency can be difficult. Use it only when you can't find the preferred frequency of the particular FSS (more on this shortly).

The airport advisory service (AAS) frequency is usually 123.6 (123.62 or 123.65 at some locations). This service provides wind, altimeter, designated runway and known traffic at non-tower airports. At part-time tower airports, the service is provided on the tower frequency when the tower is closed.

Where to look

All FSS frequencies are listed in the U.S. Government Airport/Facility Directory (A/FD), however, most of us look for these frequencies on an NOS or Jeppesen en route chart. There are major differences in how each chart lists FSS information.

Newer NOS charts depict the location of an FSS with a shadow-lined box and the frequencies for contacting the FSS are listed above the box. The preferred frequency that you should use to contact the FSS is listed first. The receive-only frequency of 122.1 (when available) is last. The common FSS frequency of 122.2 is also available when you see the shadow-lined box, but NOS omits this from the listing.

When an FSS is co-located with a VOR, frequencies and symbols for services appear above and inside the box. A thin-lined box indicates a remote communications outlet (RCO). VOR boxes without communication frequencies and an FSS name indicate that no communication with an FSS is possible over that VOR. If you have trouble remembering all of that, it's clearly laid out in the chart legend printed on every NOS en route.

On Jepp charts, FSS frequencies appear above the VOR box either when voice is available over the VOR or when the FSS has an RCO at that location. Otherwise, the FSS and its frequencies are listed above the corresponding airport or location name. The first two numbers of the frequency are omitted, e.g., 122.1 is listed as 2.1, 122.2 is 2.2, etc. The controlling FSS is listed next to the available frequencies.

One-way frequencies, that is transmit only or receive only, are noted on NOS charts with an R (FSS can receive only) or T (FSS can transmit only). On Jepp charts, it's noted with a G (FSS guards/receives only). In this situation, you must listen on the appropriate VOR frequency and remember to turn up the volume on the VOR receiver.

Communications

When contacting an FSS en route, keep the following procedures in mind:

• When talking to ATC, don't leave the frequency without first asking the controller. If possible, pick a time when there's a lull in activities. Don't wait until you're in heavy weather or dense traffic. Give yourself time to develop alternate plans in case the weather deteriorates.
• Once on the FSS frequency, listen for a moment. Don't transmit over someone else.
• Give the complete aircraft identification and your approximate position so FSS personnel can respond on the appropriate transmitter.
• State the frequency you're using. Many FSSs monitor up to 10 different frequencies.
• Give FSS personnel a chance to respond before proceeding with your request. They might be busy with someone else.

Flight Watch

The en route flight advisory service, more commonly known as Flight Watch, should be used only for weather advisories, such as weather trends, hazards, and weather forecast variations for that segment of your flight between climb-out and descent. Flight Watch should not to be used for initial briefings, selected weather reports, position reports, flight plan filing, nor to obtain notams, frequencies, etc.

Always give pireps to Flight Watch whenever possible, since these are disseminated almost immediately into the FSS system. On the other hand, pireps given to ATC aren't always passed along.

Flight Watch normally operates from 6 a.m. to 10 p.m. local time on 122.0 MHz. The FSS associated with each center operates Flight Watch. You can usually talk to Flight Watch if you're at least 5000 feet agl, occasionally lower (terrain permitting). Separate Flight Watch frequencies are now available for aircraft flying at and above Flight Level 180. Frequencies and outlets can be found in the A/FD and on the en route charts.

   To contact Flight Watch, simply call the name of the Flight Watch facility that corresponds to the center's airspace in which you're located. For example, if you're in Cleveland Center's area, call Cleveland Flight Watch on 122.0 at or above 5000 feet agl. This way, you don't have to hunt for the appropriate FSS to call, just look at the center boundaries on the en route chart. Jeppesen lists Flight Watch information above the navaid box and includes the identifier of the controlling FSS.

Flight Watch communications

Since Flight Watch uses only one frequency below 18,000 feet, congestion is a problem. Follow the FSS contact procedures mentioned previously and:

• If possible, use the name of the Flight Watch facility, e.g., Cleveland Flight Watch, otherwise, Flight Watch alone is sufficient.
• Give your position in relation to an identifiable landmark or navaid. An exact position isn't required, but they do need a general location in order to use the appropriate transmitter.
• Give your cruising altitude, route, destination and IFR capability before stating your request.Flight Watch can help locate smoother air, provide information on severe weather, cloud tops, icing, etc.

Other services

In addition to Flight Watch, the following in-flight weather advisories are provided: weather advisory broadcasts by FSS, and severe weather forecast alerts broadcast by center. These advisories contain information on severe weather, convective sigmets, sigmets and airmets when within 150 miles of the broadcasting FSS or within 150 miles of a particular center's airspace.

Hiwas available

Hazardous in-flight weather advisory service (HIWAS) is a continuous broadcast of summarized severe weather forecast alerts, sigmets, convective sigmets, airmets and urgent pireps. Hiwas is broadcast over selected VORs and is indicated on NOS charts by the solid square in the lower right corner of the VOR box (see Figure 3 below). Jeppesen lists HIWAS over the FSS frequencies where available. These broadcasts are slowly taking the place of the in-flight weather advisories mentioned earlier.

Index